WORKBOOK

AMANDA MARIS

INTERMEDIATE
OUTCOMES

HEINLE
CENGAGE Learning™

Australia • Brazil • Japan • Korea • Mexico • Singapore • Spain • United Kingdom • United States

Outcomes *Intermediate Workbook*
Amanda Maris

Publisher: Jason Mann

Commissioning Editor: John Waterman

Project Manager: Karen Jamieson

Development Editor: Karen Jamieson

Product Manager: Ruth McAleavey

Head of Production: Alissa Chappell

Production Controller: Paul Herbert

Cover and text designer: Studio April

Compositor: Pre-PressPMG

ISBN: 978-1-4240-2797-2

Heinle, Cengage Learning EMEA
Cheriton House, North Way, Andover, Hampshire
SP10 5BE United Kingdom

Cengage Learning is a leading provider of customised learning solutions with office locations around the globe, including Singapore, the United Kingdom, Australia, Mexico, Brazil and Japan. Locate our local office at **international.cengage.com/region**

Cengage Learning products are represented in Canada by Nelson Education Ltd.

Visit Heinle online at **elt.heinle.com**
Visit our corporate website at **cengage.com**

Photo credits

Although every effort has been made to contact copyright holders before publication, this has not always been possible. If notified, the publisher will undertake to rectify any errors or omissions at the earliest opportunity.

Alamy: pp41 (MBI / Alamy), 83tr (Images of Africa Photobank / Alamy), 83b (World Pictures / Alamy), 89t (Patagonik Works / Alamy), 102b (Roger Bamber / Alamy)

The Bridgeman Art Library: 89b (Velazquez, Diego Rodriguez de Silva y (1599-1660) / Prado, Madrid, Spain / Giraudon / The Bridgeman Art Library)

Getty Images: 23 (Joel Sartore), 31 (Duncan Baxter/Stringer), 57 (Dan Koeck/Contributor), 65 (WireImage), 77a (Troy Aossey), 77c (Sheer Photo, Inc), 77d (Image Source), 77e (mother image), 77f (Digital Vision), 80 (Duncan McKenzie), 83tl (Bill Curtsinger), 83m (Jens Kuhfs), 87 (Art Vandalay), 99 (Getty Images), 101 (Lucy Claxton), 102t (GettyImages), 102b (Shaun Egan), 103 (Sony Music Archive/Getty Images)

iStockphoto.com: 8 (Chris Schmidt), 10 (Adam Korzekwa), 13, 14a, 14b (Peter Finnie), 14c (Eric Hood), 14d, 14e (Ron Hohenhaus), 14f (Jennifer Trenchard), 14g (Catherine Lane), 17t (Pascal Genest), 17b-a (Chris Hepburn), 17b-b (Sandra O'Claire), 17b-c, 17b-d (onur kocamaz), 17b-e (Liza McCorkle), 20 (Martin Strmiska), 21, 24 (Michael Westhoff), 25 (Vladimir Sazonov), 27 (José Luis Gutiérrez), 29 (Sami Suni), 33 (Sean Locke), 43 (adrian beesley), 44a (Justin Horrocks), 44b (Lise Gagne), 44c (Lisa F. Young), 44d (Chris Schmidt), 44e (Francisco Romero), 44f (Justin Horrocks), 46 (Nicholas Sutcliffe), 47, 52 (Daniel Bendjy), 54 (Chris Schmidt), 53, 58 (David Joyner), 70 (Tobias Helbig), 71a (Noam Armonn), 71b (Justin Horrocks), 71c (arne thaysen), 71d (Andy Medina), 72 (Rob Sylvan), 75 (Donna Coleman), 77b (Carme Balcells), 79 (Carme Balcells), 83a (Michel de Nijs), 90 (Daniel Halvorson), 95 (Kevin Russ)

Shutterstock.com: 62 (Francesco Dazzi)

Artwork

Mark Draisey pp. 14, 24, 50, 65, Mark Duffin p. 19, 34, KJA Artists pp 36, 89

Page 34 'Grammar: Exercise C'. From 'Ten stupidest laws are named.' http://www.telegraph.co.uk/news/uknews/1568475/Ten-stupidest-laws-are-named.html, Copyright © Telegraph Group Limited, London 2008.

Page 57 The man who traded a paperclip for a house, Copyright © Kyle MacDonald, http://oneredpaperclip.blogspot.com/

Page 83 'Lost destinations now back on the list' from '10 Journeys for the 21st Century' By Paul Simpson, http://www.wanderlust.co.uk/article.php?page_id=96 Copyright © www.wanderlust.co.uk, 2007.

The publishers would like to thank the following sources for permission to reproduce their copyright protected texts:

Page 34 'Grammar: Exercise C'. From 'Ten stupidest laws are named.' http://www.telegraph.co.uk/news/uknews/1568475/Ten-stupidest-laws-are-named.html <http://www.telegraph.co.uk/news/uknews/1568475/Ten-stupidest-laws-are-named.html> , Copyright © Telegraph Group Limited <https://cmsproweb.thomsonlearning.com:4502/rms/action/editDirectory?directory_id=183128> , London 2008.

Page 57 The man who traded a paperclip for a house, Copyright © Kyle MacDonald, http://oneredpaperclip.blogspot.com/ <http://oneredpaperclip.blogspot.com/>

Page 83 'Lost destinations now back on the list' from '10 Journeys for the 21st Century' By Paul Simpson, http://www.wanderlust.co.uk/article.php?page_id=96 <http://www.wanderlust.co.uk/article.php?page_id=96> Copyright © www.wanderlust.co.uk <http://www.wanderlust.co.uk/> , 2007.

Printed in Singapore
1 2 3 4 5 6 7 8 9 10 – 12 11 10

CONTENTS

GRAMMAR Question formation

A Write questions that you might ask another student at the beginning of a new class.

1 What / name?
   What's your name? ....

2 Where / from?
   ....

3 What / do?
   ....

4 What / do / when / not work?
   ....

5 How long / study / English?
   ....

6 Why / learn / English?
   ....

7 study / here / before?
   ....

8 meet / the teacher / yet?
   ....

9 What / think of / the test we did?
   ....

10 What / go / do / after this class?
   ....

B Match the answers (a–j) to the questions (1–10) in A.

a .... I'm not sure. Maybe we could go for a coffee.

b .... Alava. It's a small town in the north of Spain.

c .... No, never. It's my first time in a school in the UK.

d .... I'm into cooking and spending time with my family.

e .... The grammar was OK but I was nervous in the speaking test.

f .... I work in the wine industry.

g .... About five years, on and off.

h ...*1*... Magda, short for Magdalena.

i .... Yes, she seems very nice.

j .... I need it for my job. Most of our foreign clients speak English.

C Nick is thinking of doing a course at an international language centre. Complete his questions to the receptionist. Use the correct form of the verbs in brackets.

N: Hi. Could you give me some information on your Russian courses?

R: Yeah, sure. Take a seat. What would you like to know?

N: Well, what [1]................... a typical class .... ? (involve)

R: Well, it varies, but there is always a range of activities, with lots of speaking practice.

N: So how many students [2]................... there in a class? (be)

R: A maximum of 12.

N: And where [3]................... they .... ? (come from)

R: All over the world. We have about 30 different nationalities at any one time.

N: And how long [4]................... each class .... ? (last)

R: About 50 minutes, longer if it's an intensive course.

N: How [5]................... you .... on a student's level? (decide)

R: Apart from beginners, there's a written test and also an oral – so that we know how good you are at speaking and understanding.

N: What qualifications [6]................... the teachers .... (have), if you don't mind me asking?

R: No, it's a good question. All our teachers are native speakers and most of them have lots of experience.

N: OK, fair enough. I've used quite a few books already so which ones [7]................... you .... (go / use) in the next course?

R: Well, it depends on the class. In intensive courses we use a wide range of different materials. Some of them we develop ourselves.

N: OK. One last question, how much [8]................... the course .... ? (cost)

R: It depends. Let me get you a price list.

N: OK, great, thanks.

D Choose the correct words in italics in the quiz opposite. Then see if you know the answers to the questions.

Language note subject questions

If a question asks about the subject of a sentence, the verb has the same form as a statement, e.g.
***Who** in the class **speaks** Italian? **Katie**.*
(= the subject of speaks)
NOT ~~Who in the class does speak Italian?~~

LANGUAGES QUIZ

1 *Which / What* language *does use / uses* the Cyrillic alphabet?
☐ Polish　　☐ Russian　　☐ French

2 How *many / much* living languages *exist / do exist* in the world today?
☐ about 6,000　　☐ about 600　　☐ about 60

3 *Why / How* do you *write / writing* Hebrew and Arabic?
☐ from left to right　　☐ from right to left　　☐ from top to bottom

4 *When / Where* does the word 'alphabet' originally *comes / come* from?
☐ Egyptian hieroglyphics
☐ the name of the first dictionary writer
☐ the first two letters of the Greek alphabet

5 *What / How* percentage of the Internet *is / are* in English?
☐ 56 per cent　　☐ 86 per cent　　☐ 99 per cent

6 *What / Who did create / created* the first computer programming language?
☐ an American businessman　　☐ a German engineer　　☐ a British academic

DEVELOPING CONVERSATIONS Asking follow-up questions

Use the questions in the box to complete the conversations. There is one extra question each time.

> What year are you in?
> How long have you been learning it?
> Whose class were you in?
> What are you studying?
> Whereabouts?

A A: Where are you from?
B: Hungary.
A: Oh, really? [1]................... ?
B: A town called Szeged. Have you heard of it?
A: No, sorry, I haven't. Have you studied here before?
B: No, never.
A: But your English is really good. [2]................... ?
B: About seven years, on and off. But it's a lot of work, with my degree course, too.
A: Oh, [3]................... ?
B: Medicine.
A: Really, me too. [4]................... ?
B: I've just finished my second year.

> How many brothers and sisters have you got?
> What do they do?
> What did you do?
> Did you get anything nice?
> Older or younger?

B A: Hi, again. Did you have a good weekend?
B: Yes, thanks. It was fun.
A: [1]................... ?
B: I went with my sister to London. She's over from Italy at the moment. We went shopping.
A: [2]................... ?
B: She bought some presents for everyone at home.
A: Oh yes. [3]................... ?
B: Three sisters and a brother. What about you?
A: Just one brother.
B: [4]................... ?
A: The same age – in fact we're twins!

> What kind of music are you into?
> Where are you doing that?
> Do you enjoy it?
> So why are you studying English?
> Where do you work?

C A: What do you do?
B: I'm a student, from Argentina. I'm studying Law.
A: Oh, [1]................... ?
B: The University of Buenos Aires.
A: OK. [2]................... ?
B: I want to do international law. What about you?
A: I'm in computing.
B: Right. [3]................... ?
A: At a programming company in Frankfurt.
B: So what do you do when you're not working?
A: I'm a DJ in a club.
B: Really? [4]................... ?
A: All sorts really – funk, jazz, hip-hop.

VOCABULARY Learning languages

Replace the <u>underlined</u> words with the expressions in the box.

get by	teach myself
fairly fluent	picked it up
my level is very basic	to speak slowly
I am more or less bilingual	
maintain conversations on a range of topics	

1 I've only just taken it up, so <u>I can't say very much</u>. When people talk to me, I always have to ask them <u>not to speak so fast</u>.
2 I'm trying to <u>learn at home</u> from a book and some CDs, but it's slow progress.
3 I can <u>survive in the language</u> in basic conversations.
4 I'm <u>quite good at the language</u> and most native speakers can understand me. I <u>learnt it without formal lessons</u> by living there in the 1970s.
5 I've been studying for a few years now so I can <u>talk about a lot of subjects</u>.
6 My dad was born in Milan and my mum's Scottish, so <u>I speak both languages pretty much perfectly</u>.

Language note word order with phrasal verbs

- -

Remember the word order when you use a pronoun with separable verbs:
I **picked up** my Spanish while travelling. OR
I **picked my** Spanish **up** while travelling. BUT
I **picked** it **up** while travelling. NOT
~~I picked up it while travelling.~~

VOCABULARY Language words

A Look at the <u>underlined</u> words. What type of word is each one?

I've just ¹<u>taken up</u> painting at our local art college. To be honest, I'm no Van Gogh. Doing anything ²<u>for</u> the first time is ³<u>hard</u> and people always want to do ⁴<u>well</u>. But my ⁵<u>advice</u> is to concentrate on the activity. What I ⁶<u>mean</u> is, enjoy what ⁷<u>you</u> are doing and don't worry about the end result. And never compare yourself with anyone else. There will always be those ⁸<u>annoyingly</u> talented people who can ⁹<u>take</u> on any new challenge and succeed. Ignore them.

1 *phrasal verb*	2	3 ....
4	5	6 ....
7	8	9 ....

B Answer the questions and test your knowledge.

1 What's the opposite of these words and expressions? Circle the correct option.
easy – *hard / hardly*
slowly – *fastly / fast*
fluent – *unfluent / not very fluent*
a minor mistake – a *serious / large* mistake
good progress – *slow / bad* progress
a basic level of Japanese – *a high / tall* level of Japanese

2 Do these words collocate with *make* or *do*?

a mistake	an exercise	progress
your homework	a course	a fool of yourself
a good job	an effort	

3 Write the correct prepositions.
worry .... your progress rely .... your best friend
concentrate .... work deal .... a problem

4 Where is the stress on these words?
evidence motivation environment
bilingual continuity embarrassed

5 What do these words have in common?
honest knowledge write foreign

LISTENING

🎧 1.1 You are going to hear Trisha and Andy talking about a change in Trisha's life. Choose the correct answers, a, b, or c.
1 What course has Trisha decided to go on?
   a a foreign language
   b knitting
   c building skills
2 What is Andy's reaction to her news?
   a He's impressed.
   b He wants to try something new too.
   c He criticises her.
3 What was the problem at the first class?
   a All the other students were men.
   b Trisha didn't know the answer to a question.
   c Trisha said something silly.
4 What will Trisha do in the first term?
   a whatever she likes
   b general skills
   c bricklaying
5 Trisha thinks her new job will be
   a well paid
   b interesting
   c hard work

PRONUNCIATION Silent letters

A Underline the silent letters in these extracts from the listening.
1 I've signed up for a building course
2 an evening course in a foreign language or knitting or whatever
3 there's a need for builders and plumbers
4 the first class was a bit nerve-wracking
5 I felt such a fool and I went bright red

B ✷ 1.2 Listen and check.

READING

A Read the chat room posts quickly. What question are they answering?
a Where's the best place to learn a second language?
b Where's the strangest place you've had a language class?
c Why do you like learning languages?

B Read the posts again. Write the correct names.
Who …
1 didn't think they would learn much? ....Mike........
2 still remembers what they learnt? ....
3 was surprised by how much they knew? ....
4 wanted to improve on their current level? ....
5 didn't know specific vocabulary? ....
6 wasn't learning with a teacher? ....
7 practiced again soon after the class? ....

C Complete the sentences with the missing prepositions. Look back at the posts if you need to.
1 It's funny how I forget some words but others stay .... me.
2 An intensive course is a good way to top .... your English.
3 I went .... to a German class with a friend and really enjoyed it.
4 The most difficult thing is often starting .... a conversation.
5 Where can I sign .... for Italian classes?
6 We'd like to find .... about Russian classes in our area.

It wasn't really a class but I learnt a lot of words. Many years ago, I was on a cycling holiday in a remote part of Spain and I had an accident. I was taken to the nearest A&E department, where no-one spoke English. I could get by with everyday Spanish, but didn't know any medical words. The staff looked after me and, by the time I left, I knew the words for all the parts of the leg and how to describe pain in Spanish. And it has stayed with me to this day!
Alex, US

On a ferry, of all places. We were on our way to France from the UK and suddenly a French lady appeared and gave us a leaflet about a language class on board. I must admit I was a bit sceptical about how much we could pick up in such a short time. But there was nothing much else to do so we went along. We practised ordering things in a shop and café, and it was great fun. The best thing was actually using the language on the other side of the Channel.
Mike, UK

Not a class in the usual sense but I got a lot of speaking practice in a tunnel in Japan! I was on a packed train using my *teach yourself Japanese* book and CD. What I really wanted was to speak to a real person but I didn't feel confident to start up a conversation and everyone was very reserved. Suddenly, we broke down in the middle of a long tunnel. It was such an unusual thing that it got everyone talking. I found out that I knew more than I thought.
Cerys, Wales

Under the stars! A new language school had opened in my town and I was really keen to sign up. I thought learning English with a native speaker would help me top up what I already knew from school. I arrived for the first class and found the place in darkness. The electricity had failed but rather than cancel the classes, the teachers used different spaces outside the school. All the local cafés were full of other students, so we ended up on the beach. It was a strange first lesson but it really broke the ice.
Lydia, Greece

> ### Glossary
> **A&E:** Accident and Emergency
> **the Channel:** the sea that separates England from France

GRAMMAR Narrative tenses

A **Complete the gapped sentence to link the two actions. Write one verb in the past simple and one verb in the past perfect.**

1 The German class started. I arrived.
When I *arrived, the German class had* already *started* .

2 I didn't recognise her. We met a few times before.
Although we .... , ...

3 She went bright red. She used the wrong word.
After she .... , ...

4 Mike was late for the class. He left his books at home.
Mike .... because ....

5 Ana spent an hour in the advanced class. She realised she was in the wrong room.
Ana .... before ....

6 I realised he was the boss. I asked him to make me a coffee.
By the time .... , ...

B **Complete the anecdote by putting the verbs in brackets into the correct tense. Use narrative tenses.**

I remember my first driving lesson like it was yesterday. I ¹...................... (just / have) my 17th birthday when my parents ²...................... (say) I could start learning to drive. My older sister ³...................... (already / pass) her test and she ⁴...................... (save) to buy her first car. On the morning of the lesson, I was really nervous. I ⁵...................... (not sleep) very well the night before and I ⁶...................... (feel) a bit sick. Then there was a knock at the door – my instructor ⁷...................... (arrive).
He talked me through the controls and gave me really clear instructions. A few minutes later, We ⁸...................... (drive) round a quiet part of town when I ⁹...................... (see) a friend out of the corner of my eye. He waved at me and – without thinking – I waved back. The car ¹⁰...................... (move) towards a tree when the instructor ¹¹...................... (grab) the wheel. 'Keep your eyes on the road!' he shouted. I went bright red and couldn't believe what I ¹²...................... (just / do). When we ¹³...................... (drive) home, I ¹⁴...................... (not say) a word. I ¹⁵...................... (concentrate) hard so that I didn't make another mistake. It was the longest journey of my life!

GRAMMAR
Other uses of the past continuous

Match the sentence halves.
1 I'm so tired today. I ......
2 Is there a problem with your mobile? I ......
3 Sorry we're late. We ......
4 What's the matter with the dog? It ......
5 We didn't see much of the area because it ......
6 Marcus lost his job because he ......
7 I'm a bit worried about Lucy. She ......
8 Phil had a brilliant job. He ......

a was crying nearly all day yesterday.
b was trying to get through to you all day yesterday.
c was training young racing drivers in Milan.
d was taking a lot of time off to visit his girlfriend.
e was raining all week.
f was barking for hours earlier today.
g were waiting for a bus for ages.
h was working on an essay until two in the morning.

DEVELOPING CONVERSATIONS
John was telling me ...

Number the lines in the correct order to make three conversations.

1 No, I have private lessons. My tutor is really good – very patient. ......
Is he? So, what style do you play? ......
Yeah, that's right. ......
Amy was telling me you've taken up the guitar. ...*1*..
Classical. I like listening to rock but don't think I'm a Jimi Hendrix type! ......
Great! Are you teaching yourself to play? ......

2 Well, if I hear of anything, I'll let you know. ......
No, but I've only just started looking. ......
Yes, that's right. ......
Like a waiter or something? ......
Have you had any luck yet? ......
Paul was telling me you're looking for a part-time job. ......
Yes. ......
Well, maybe restaurant or bar work. ......
What sort of job are you looking for? ......

3 How long will you be away for? ......
Yes, news travels fast! ......
Well, good luck, I hope it goes well. ......
About twelve months, I think. ......
Katrina was telling me you're going to Argentina. ......
I've got a job in a language school. ......
That's amazing. What are you going to do? ......

DEVELOPING WRITING
An anecdote – checking tenses

A Correct the mistakes in a student's first draft.

I'll never forget the first time I had to give a presentation. I ¹ studied English at the time and it was part of my course. It ² was taking me a long time to choose my topic, but then I came up with a good idea. I ³ was always been interested in clothes, so I decided to talk about the fashion industry. ⁴ During I was preparing the talk, I ⁵ was doing a lot of research on the Internet. The evening before my presentation, I ⁶ were working until about 2 a.m. ⁷ Until I got to my class, I ⁸ have carefully printed out my notes and rehearsed my talk in front of the mirror. A classmate was also going to give her talk and she went first. Imagine my horror when she said, 'Today I'm going to talk to you about the fashion industry.' My heart sank. I was so angry with myself. I had spoken to her the week before the presentation but hadn't ⁹ check what she ¹⁰ chosen as her topic.

B Write an anecdote (120–150 words) about when you did something for the first time. Use one of these ideas or an idea of your own.

The first day
- at a new school
- in a new job
- on a new course

The first time you
- cooked a meal for someone special
- went on a date
- went abroad
- gave a speech / presentation

Learner tip

Plan your ideas and then write the first draft quickly. Go back and check your writing, correcting mistakes and looking for ways to improve the language.

Vocabulary Builder Quiz 1 (OVB pp2–4)

Try the *OVB* quiz for Unit 1. Write your answers in your notebook. Then check them and record your score.

A What's the opposite of 'a strong accent'?

B Match 1–5 and a–e to form compound nouns.
1 tourist   a policy
2 working   b teacher
3 head   c seat
4 window   d environment
5 health   e trade

C Which word do you need to complete the sentences in each set?
1 I got .... marks in the test. / You get great views from the .... floor. / Who's the .... salesman in the company?
2 I never seem to have any .... time. / You can stay over in our .... room. / Where's the .... key for the garage?
3 You need good computer .... in this job. / My boss has got no people .... at all. / It's never too late to learn new ....

D Complete the verbs that begin with *re...* .
1 It's Lucy's birthday. Re............ me to buy her a card.
2 We've sent them several emails but they never re............
3 They're going to re............ the decision to build a new airport.
4 I never read newspapers that re............ private information about celebrities.
5 Don't worry. You can re............ on me to look after things while you're away.

E Choose the correct words.
1 I'm going to miss the film. My train is *rushing / running* late.
2 I need to *progress / improve* my language skills.
3 She's a bit boring. It's hard to *keep / maintain* the conversation going.
4 Don't *remind / remember* me about getting his name wrong. It was so embarrassing.
5 My new job *involves / provides* a lot of paperwork.

F Change the words in brackets so that they are in the correct form to complete the text.
'I've just taken up Italian lessons – again. I did a course a few years ago but there wasn't much ¹ (improve) in my level of ² (fluent). My big problem then was time ³ (manage). I was working really long hours and then I didn't have much ⁴ (motivate) to go to classes or do my homework. Now, I've got more spare time and so I'm hoping I'll make more progress. I get on well with my classmates. They're all really friendly and ⁵ (chat). The ⁶ (available) of online materials is also a help. It means I can practice between lessons.'

Score ___ /25

Wait a couple of weeks and try the quiz again.
Compare your scores.

02 FEELINGS

VOCABULARY Feelings

A How are these people feeling? Match the adjectives with the speakers 1–7.

relaxed	guilty	disappointed	exhausted
pleased	confused	annoyed	

> I feel really bad about losing Mum's favourite ring. How on earth am I going to tell her?

> I don't get this. The map says number 24 is opposite the pizza place, but all I can see is a big block of flats.

> I can't move a muscle and I could sleep for a week. That's the last time I go cycling with Alex.

> I really expected to get that job. I've got all the qualifications and loads of experience. I couldn't believe it when they said no.

> I love the peace and quiet here. You can just forget all the stresses of everyday life.

> This is just a nightmare! They say we can't have a refund. I'm going to complain to the manager.

> A new iPod! That's just what I wanted. Thanks, that's really kind of you.

B Complete the conversations with the pairs of words and phrases.

upset / worried	down / fed up
in such a bad mood / furious	terrible / stressed

1. A: Are you OK?
   B: No, I feel .... at the moment. I'm so .... out at work that I can't sleep at night.
2. A: Is Magda OK? I think she's been crying.
   B: She's .... because her sister's in hospital. She must be really .... about her.
3. A: Why are you .... ?
   B: I crashed my dad's sports car last night and he's absolutely .... with me.
4. A: Don't speak to Eddie. He isn't in a very good mood today.
   B: How come he's so .... ?
   A: He hasn't scored a goal for weeks and he says he's really .... with training.

GRAMMAR *Be, look, seem, etc.*

Complete the chat room messages with the pairs of words. Put the linking verbs in the correct form.

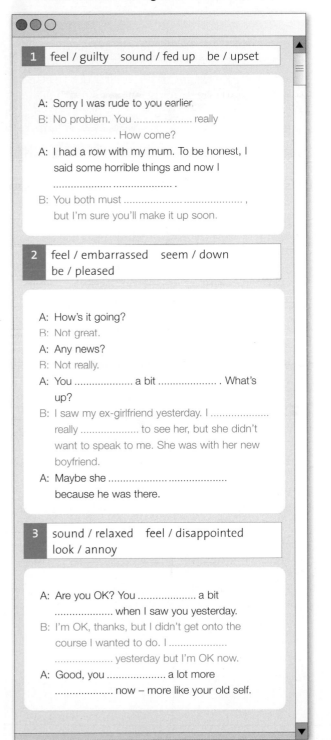

1 feel / guilty   sound / fed up   be / upset

A: Sorry I was rude to you earlier.
B: No problem. You .... really
.... How come?
A: I had a row with my mum. To be honest, I said some horrible things and now I
....
B: You both must .... ,
but I'm sure you'll make it up soon.

2 feel / embarrassed   seem / down
be / pleased

A: How's it going?
B: Not great.
A: Any news?
B: Not really.
A: You .... a bit .... What's up?
B: I saw my ex-girlfriend yesterday. I .... really .... to see her, but she didn't want to speak to me. She was with her new boyfriend.
A: Maybe she ....
because he was there.

3 sound / relaxed   feel / disappointed
look / annoy

A: Are you OK? You .... a bit .... when I saw you yesterday.
B: I'm OK, thanks, but I didn't get onto the course I wanted to do. I .... yesterday but I'm OK now.
A: Good, you .... a lot more .... now – more like your old self.

DEVELOPING CONVERSATIONS
Response expressions

Match the news (1–6) with the responses (a–f).
1 My laptop has been stolen. ......
2 I've just passed my driving test. ......
3 I'm afraid I can't come to your party. ......
4 My sister's getting married. ......
5 My dad has just lost his job. ......
6 My grandmother is coming out of hospital tomorrow. ......

a Really? Congratulations! You can give me a lift to work!
b Wow! That's great. When is the wedding?
c Oh, no! I'm sorry. I'm sure he'll find a new one soon.
d Oh, no, what a pain! Have you lost all your work?
e Phew, that's a relief. I know how worried you were.
f Oh, what a shame! I'll send you some photos.

LISTENING

A ⏺ 2.1 You are going to hear three people talking about the same event. Listen first to Mark. What event is he talking about?
a a wedding   b meeting his girlfriend's parents for the first time

B ⏺ 2.1 Listen to Mark again, and then to Mrs deVere and Annie. Are these statements true or false?
1 Before the dinner, Mark felt nervous.
2 He was wearing clothes that were too formal.
3 He felt he wasn't very good at making conversation.
4 Annie's parents already knew a lot about him.
5 Annie's parents hadn't liked her previous boyfriends.
6 Annie had forgotten to warn Mark about clothes.
7 She didn't mind that he told some jokes.
8 She was pleased that Mark had met her parents.

PRONUNCIATION Stress

A ⏺ 2.2 Underline the main stresses. Listen and check.
1 I'm not <u>normally</u> a <u>nervous person</u>, so I <u>felt pretty relaxed</u> about the <u>whole thing</u>.
2 I was wearing jeans and a shirt, but the restaurant was a really elegant place.
3 I was really fed up with Annie that she hadn't warned me it was a formal dinner.
4 To be honest, we hadn't been very keen on most of her boyfriends, so my husband and I were rather worried about the dinner.

B Listen again. Practice saying the sentences.

VOCABULARY Adjective collocations

Cross out two nouns that do not usually go with the –ing adjectives.

1 relaxing holiday / friend / weekend / massage / food
2 annoying neighbour / disaster / mobile phone ring / success / habit
3 disappointing problem / result / ending / exam grade / clothes
4 confusing atmosphere / situation / idea / explanation / skill
5 exciting sleep / development / help / news / story
6 inspiring crime / leader / speech / plan / loss

GRAMMAR -ing / -ed adjectives

A Choose the correct words.

1 You walk out of the place completely *relaxed / relaxing*. And they don't play that *annoying / annoyed* whale music, which is a relief.
2 I had to give my height, weight, and my age – it was so *embarrassed / embarrassing*. I was a bit *shocked / shocking* when I saw how much weight I'd put on.
3 I'm not sure I'm in the correct level. I'm always so *confused / confusing* at the end of the lesson. And concentrating for an hour is *exhausting / exhausted*.
4 I didn't expect it to be so beautiful. I was quite *surprising / surprised* when I saw the scenery. But our flight was delayed, which was *annoyed / annoying*.
5 I wasn't very *interested / interesting* in the characters. And the ending was *disappointed / disappointing*.

B What are the people in exercise A talking about? Match 1–5 above to a–e.

a a gym   c a trip   e a health spa
b a novel   d a language school

C Complete the conversations with the correct form of the verbs in brackets.

1 A: If you don't mind, I'd like to change channels before the news. There's an .... (interest) programme on at 8 p.m.
   B: Go ahead. I don't want to watch the news. It's always so .... (depress).
2 A: Can you believe that score – six nil? I've never been so .... (disappoint).
   B: I know. I was so .... (excite) at the start of the season.
3 A: Do you fancy coming for a walk? The view over the beach is meant to be .... (amaze).
   B: Thanks, but I'm not up to it. I feel .... (exhaust) after that journey.
4 A: Only ten people turned up to my party. I don't think I've ever been so .... (embarrass).
   B: That's a shame. It's very .... (annoy) when people let you down.

READING

A Read the article opposite quickly. What is the main reason for writing it?

a to advise people on how to improve their diet
b to explain that there is a connection between food and how people feel
c to describe a series of experiments on food

> **Learner tip**
>
> It's a good idea to read a text quickly first to get an idea of the content. Use all the information that you can see with the text (headings, photos, diagrams, etc.) to help you.

B Six parts of the article 'How food affects mood' have been removed. Write the correct letter (a–f) in the gaps in the article.

a Research also suggests that the right foods
b that activate when people enjoy themselves
c if they were eating healthily and taking regular physical exercise.
d who wrote a report based on the survey
e but felt guilty afterwards.
f There is a definite link with food and mood

C Underline the following parts of the article.

1 four mental health problems
2 the word the writer uses to describe food / drinks with a positive effect and examples of these
3 the word the writer uses to describe food / drinks with a negative effect and examples of these
4 the reason why it is important to drink enough fluid

D Which adjectives went with these nouns? Look back at the article and sentences a–f in exercise B.

1 *immediate* effect
2 .... foods
3 .... mental health
4 .... improvements
5 .... link
6 .... physical exercise

How food affects mood

Eating ice cream really does make you happy. Scientists at the Institute of Psychiatry in London tested the brains of people eating vanilla ice cream. They found an immediate effect on parts of the brain [1]... . It works on the same part of the brain that reacts when people win money or listen to music.

[2] ... can improve people's mood and even their overall mental health. A survey of 200 people found 88 per cent reported that changing their diet improved their mental health. 26 per cent said they had seen marked improvements in mood swings, 26 per cent had seen improvements in panic attacks and anxiety, and 24 per cent in depression.

People in the survey identified mood 'stressors' and 'supporters'. Eating fewer 'stressors' like chocolate, sugar, caffeine and alcohol improved their mood. They also increased the 'supporters' they ate, like water, fruit, vegetables and oily fish. Not skipping breakfast, and eating regularly also led to an increase in well-being.

Over a third of people said they were 'very certain' that the improvements to their mental health were directly linked to the changes they had made to their diet. One person who completed the survey said, '[3] ... but I do lapse and when I do, I feel noticeably different. Once you find out your triggers, you can feel so much better.'

Amanda Geary, [4] ... said 'A lot of these changes are very simple things that people can do and are fairly safe, and fit with healthy eating advice.'

Dr Wendy Doyle, a dietician, said oily fish and fruit and vegetables were known to be beneficial. 'They are good for general health – and you must have enough fluid to prevent dehydration.' She said people would also feel better [5] ... Dr Doyle added, 'People may feel bad after eating chocolate because they enjoyed eating it, [6] ... '

E Complete the sentences with the collocations from exercise D.

1 I think there's a .... between talking about your feelings and being happy.
2 I gave up strong coffee and it had an .... on me – I stopped having headaches straight away and I slept better.
3 There's been .... in my children's behaviour since they have stopped eating sugar.
4 A diet containing the .... doesn't have to be boring.
5 Many people don't realise that .... is linked to eating a good diet.
6 Taking .... , like walking or cycling, helps me deal with stress.

Glossary

mood swings: sudden changes in how you feel
skipping breakfast: avoid having breakfast
lapse: stop following good habits
triggers: things that produce a reaction

GRAMMAR Present continuous

Circle the correct form in italics.

1 A: What on earth *are you wearing / do you wear*?
   B: It's my new summer shirt. I think *it looks / it's looking* pretty cool.
   A: Well, *we meet / we're meeting* my boss later, so don't wear it then.

2 A: What *do you do / are you doing* this Saturday?
   B: *I'm going / I go* to a new yoga class. Do you fancy coming? It *sounds / is sounding* very relaxing.
   A: Sorry, I can't. *I visit / I'm visiting* my parents every Saturday.

3 A: Why on earth *are you being / do you be* so aggressive? It's unlike you.
   B: Sorry. I'm just stressed out. *I work / I'm working* on a really important project. *We're giving / We give* a presentation this afternoon and *I'm still preparing / I still prepare* my part.
   A: Oh dear. You must be a bit nervous. Good luck with it.

4 A: Cheer up. Why on earth are you so down?
   B: Don't worry. *I always feel / I'm always feeling* like this in the winter. I can't stand the short days.
   A: I know what you mean. We *normally go / are normally going* on holiday in the winter, but my kids *do / are doing* their exams soon.

Language note ... *on earth* ...

You can add ... *on earth* ... to questions to express surprise or add emphasis:
What on earth are you wearing?
Why on earth did he say that?
Where on earth have you been?

GRAMMAR Present continuous / present simple questions

Complete the pairs of questions. Use the present continuous or present simple form of the verbs in brackets.

1 How's the match ...... *going* ...... (go)? Who's ...... *winning* .... (win)?

2 What .... you .... (do) on Friday evenings? .... you .... (fancy) joining our book group?

3 Why .... you .... (cry)? .... you .... (want) to talk about it?

4 Where .... you .... (move) to? What .... (be) the new area like?

5 Why .... those people .... (stand) there? .... they .... (need) help?

6 .... your brother .... (enjoy) his new job? What exactly .... he .... (do) every day?

7 How .... your kids .... (get) to school every day? How long .... it .... (take)?

DEVELOPING CONVERSATIONS
Making excuses

Use the words to write reasons for refusing the requests.

1 A: I was wondering if you wanted to get together on Saturday?
   B: *I'd love to but I can't. I'm going away for the weekend.* (love to / but can't. go away / for the weekend.)

2 A: Can you give me a hand to set up my new computer?
   B: .... (sorry / can't. work late / this evening.)

3 A: Do you think I could use your mobile?
   B .... (afraid / can't. don't have / with me.)

4 A: Do you fancy coming to my party on Friday evening?
   B: .... (nice / of you to ask me. play in a band / every Friday.)

5 A: Would you like to meet up some time this weekend?
   B: .... (kind / of you to ask us. go to London / every weekend.)

6 A: Can you help me with my homework?
   B: .... (no / sorry. go out / this evening.)

DEVELOPING WRITING
A letter – giving news

A Rani has just started university. Complete the letter to her parents with the words in the box.

pretty	miss	settling	hug	down
sorry	into	mind	expect	out

Dear Mum and Dad

[1] .... I haven't written before, but I've been [2] .... busy since I started. I'm [3] ....in to my flat and enjoying the course so far. Lectures have started but I didn't [4] .... to be working so hard in the first month!

I've been a bit [5] .... this week. It's nothing to worry about but Rachel has changed course, so I'm now one of the few girls doing physics! I had a feeling she wasn't very happy, but I think she's sorted it [6] .... now.

I [7] .... everyone but I'm making a lot of new friends. My flatmates are all [8] .... adventure sports (my idea of hell!), but I had a go at climbing last weekend - exhausting but good fun.

My next lecture is about to start, so I'll put this in the post. Give everyone a [9] .... from me.

Lots of love

Rani
xx

P.S. If you don't [10] ...., I won't ring you on my mobile. It's too expensive - but you can ring me!

Language note
a bit / pretty / not very + adjective

- -

If you don't want to sound too negative, you can soften an adjective like this:
I'm **a bit tired**.
It was **pretty disappointing**.
It **wasn't very easy**.

B Imagine you have just left home to start a new job / go on a course. Write a letter home (120–150 words) and give your news. Use the letter in A to help you.

Vocabulary Builder Quiz 2 (*OVB* pp6–8)

Try the *OVB* quiz for Unit 2. Write your answers in your notebook. Then check them and record your score.

A Complete the phrases with a word from box A and B.

A scientific inspiring student military love–hate

B relationship accommodation campaign speech discovery

1 have a ....
2 live in ....
3 make a ....
4 give an ....
5 run a ....

B Which word do you need to complete the sentences in each set?
1 Please hold the ....
  What do I dial to get an outside ....?
  You can contact our help............. 24 hours a day.
2 You've .... spoken all evening.
  I can .... hear you over all this noise.
  There's .... any traffic in this part of town.
3 She was .... on the motorway for hours.
  I don't want to be .... indoors all weekend.
  How long were you .... in that lift?

C Cross out *up* in the sentences where it is not needed.
1 They'd been going out for ages, so I've no idea why they split up.
2 Do you think you'll get promoted up next year?
3 Cheer up – there's no need to look so sad.
4 I always throw up if I go by plane or boat.
5 When does Marcus graduate up from medical school?
6 Remember to protect up your skin by wearing suncream.

D Choose the correct words.
1 Why are you in such a bad *mood / atmosphere* today?
2 I would never *join / approach* my dad to ask for advice.
3 We left the shop because we got *fed up / upset with* waiting for the assistant.
4 They made every *intend / attempt* to save the business.
5 The next bus isn't *ahead / due* for half an hour.
6 Why did the company suffer another *lose / loss* in its profits last month?

E What form of the words in brackets do you need to complete the text?
Isn't it strange how people's feelings change? When I was in my thirties, I was very competitive at work and getting [1] (promote) was very important to me. I also hated routine and would die of [2] (bore) if I had to do the same thing more than once. Now, I might be a bit [3] (disappoint) if I don't get to the next level but it doesn't make me too miserable. I also find my work more [4] (meaning) now and I take [5] (please) in working with the same groups of people every day.

Score ___ /25

Wait a couple of weeks and try the quiz again.
Compare your scores.

VOCABULARY Places of interest

Complete the travel advice with the nouns in box A and the prepositions in box B.

A	theme park	square	galleries	ruins	lake
	old town	market	mosque	palace	castle

B	by	out	along	about	outside

TRAVELLERS' TIPS

culture vultures

THIS SUMMER the royal ¹....*palace*.... is open to the public for the first time with exhibitions of paintings from across the centuries. There are also a number of private ²................... in the city with paintings for sale.

FOR LOVERS of architecture, head to the ³................... with its interesting mix of historic buildings. ⁴................... in the east of the city, is the site of the old Jewish district. It also has a number of beautiful churches and the city ⁵................... .

TAKE A TRIP out to the Roman ⁶................... and learn about some of the first people to live in the area. Local archaeologists give talks at the weekends.

for kids of all ages

CHECK OUT SkyFlyer, the tallest roller coaster in the country, at the new ⁷................... . It's ⁸................... 45 minutes ⁹................... the city but it's well worth the trip.

EXPLORE the medieval ¹⁰................... and try your hand at ghost-hunting. The west tower is supposed to be haunted by a murdered prince.

For a **MORE RELAXING** time, take a boat out on the ¹¹................... . Swimming isn't allowed but you can enjoy a picnic down ¹²................... the water.

fun on a budget

IF MONEY IS A BIT TIGHT, join a free walking tour. Local residents act as guides and give an insider view of the city. All tours start in the main ¹³................... under the clock tower.

DON'T MISS the ¹⁴................... on Fridays and Saturdays with stalls all ¹⁵................... the High Street. You'll find everything from cheap and tasty snacks to local souvenirs at bargain prices.

DEVELOPING CONVERSATIONS
Recommendations

Kim is talking to her Mexican friend, Felix, about a possible holiday. Write the correct letters for the missing lines in the conversation. There is one line that you do not need.

> a Oh, I'd love to but I can't.
> b Jo isn't really a big fan of sunbathing, to be honest.
> c OK, well in that case, how about something more cultural?
> d That would be great, thanks.
> e It depends on what you like.
> f And you could always have a go at some water sports.
> g ~~My boyfriend Jo and I are thinking of going to Mexico this year.~~

Kim ¹..*g*.. Can you recommend anywhere good to go?

Felix Well, Mexico is a big country and there are lots of places to choose from. ²...... If you want a relaxing holiday, there are some fantastic beaches all along the Caribbean coast.

Kim ³...... And I'm not really into it either.

Felix ⁴...... There are amazing Mayan ruins throughout the area.

Kim That sounds interesting. I think I saw a documentary about them on TV. They look like pyramids but with steps. Is that right?

Felix Well, some of them are pyramids. Others are more like houses, or even palaces.

Kim Wow! That sounds amazing.

Felix ⁵...... There are lots of places for diving or snorkelling. You could also try kayaking if you like.

Kim Oh, that's my idea of heaven!

Felix OK, I can do an online check for the best places for doing that, if you want.

Kim ⁶......

DEVELOPING WRITING An email – giving advice

A **Dan has emailed his friend, Yuko, with some advice about his home town. Number the content of his message in order.**

suggestions of other things to do	......
ending	......
reason for writing	......
practical advice	......
greeting	..*1*..
where to go first	......

B **Complete the email with the words in the box.**

time	quick	at	take	anyway	straight
during	down				

○●○○

Hi Yuko,

Just a ¹.....*quick*..... note to say I'm sorry I can't see you next week. I'm on a training course, but here are a few ideas of things to do ².................. your stay.

The old town is a good place to start. You can just wander round and soak up the atmosphere. If you want to ³.................. photos, head to the castle ruins and you'll find some amazing views.

Don't miss the parade on Saturday. It's a great laugh. They have decorated floats, people in fancy dress, and bands playing music. It starts ⁴.................. midday in the main square.

I know you're a fan of roller coasters, so check out the new theme park, Adventure Zone. It's about an hour outside of town, but you can get a bus ⁵.................. there.

Don't forget to buy a travel card. It's the cheapest way to get around the area. The best places to eat are ⁶.................. by the old canal. They're pretty cheap but the food is good.

⁷.................. , hope this information helps. Have a great ⁸.................. .

All the best,
Dan

C **Cross out the word or phrase that doesn't collocate.**

1 Have a great *week* / *time off* / *time*.
2 You can *ride* / *get* / *take* a bus to the castle.
3 I know you are *like* / *into* / *a fan of* old churches.
4 The festival is *great fun* / *a great laugh* / *funny*.
5 The show starts *at 2pm* / *every day* / *on Wednesday*.
6 The best places *to eat* / *for food* / *for eating* are in the man square.

D **Match the sentence halves.**

1 If you're into art, head ......
2 The comedy festival starts on Friday, so don't ......
3 Local transport isn't great. It's difficult to get ......
4 If you have some spending money, check ......
5 When you want to relax, go to the beach and soak ......
6 Don't try the restaurants in the centre. They're pretty ......
7 Take lots of photos and don't ......
8 It's nice to wander ......

a out the new shopping mall.
b to the new gallery in the main square.
c round the market on a Sunday morning.
d forget to send me copies.
e around after midnight apart from in a taxi.
f up some sunshine.
g miss it. It's a great laugh.
h expensive and you have to book.

E **Write an email in 120–150 words for the following situation. Use the checklist in exercise A and the language in this section to help you.**
An English-speaking friend is spending a week's holiday in your home town. You are going to be away, so write an email to your friend giving advice about their stay.

Learner tip

Try to keep your reader interested when you write. Vary the language you use so that your sentences don't all sound the same, e.g. instead of saying *try* or *go to* all the time, use language like *check out*, *head to, don't miss, don't forget to*, etc.

VOCABULARY Holiday problems

A Correct the <u>underlined</u> mistakes.

1 What a nightmare! Our flight was <u>delay</u> and we were <u>stucked</u> at the airport for hours.
2 I'm never going on holiday with my family again. My brother and sister didn't stop <u>argue</u> all week.
3 We must go somewhere warm next year. It poured <u>of</u> rain and it was so <u>wind</u> all week.
4 I must look like a tourist. Everywhere we went we got ripped <u>up</u>. I paid €15 for a beer!
5 A couple took our <u>part</u> on the beach and Jim got really <u>anger</u> with them. It was so embarrassing!
6 Never again! The beach was so <u>crowd</u> you couldn't even see the sand.
7 The kids were ill on the plane. Jodi threw <u>off</u> three times. Poor thing!

B Complete the conversations with the pairs of words in the box. Put the verbs in the past simple.

steal / passport	spoil / trip	miss / flight
lose / camera	charge / a fortune	
have / upset stomach		

1 A: Did you have a good holiday?
   B: Not really. We came home early.
   A: How come?
   B: We all ...... *had* ...... an ...... *upset stomach* ...... and couldn't eat thing. That was our only holiday this year and it really .... the ....

2 A: I'm exhausted. The journey back was a nightmare.
   B: How come?
   A: Well we .... our .... to Heathrow and the next plane landed at 3 a.m. The taxi driver .... us .... to take us home – over £100.
   B: Oh no, what a pain!

3 A: You seem a bit fed up.
   B: Yeah well, I've just had the holiday from hell.
   A: What happened?
   B: Well, I expected a nice relaxing week, but I spent the first night at the police station because someone .... my .... I took loads of photos but then I .... my .... on the last day. It's just so disappointing.
   A: Oh, what a shame!

LISTENING

🔊 3.1 You are going to hear five people talking about holiday problems. Match the speakers (1–5) to the letters (a–e).

a It cost a lot more than we had expected.
b We had several transport problems.
c The local attractions were awful.
d We didn't get on with each other very well.
e There were too many other people.

Speaker 1 ☐   Speaker 4 ☐
Speaker 2 ☐   Speaker 5 ☐
Speaker 3 ☐

PRONUNCIATION Same sound or different?

A Are the letters in bold the same sound (S) or different (D)?

1 The hotel s**ou**nded wonderful. / The terminal was so cr**ow**ded.   [S]
2 There was only a th**eme** park. / There were q**ueue**s everywhere.   ☐
3 We had b**oo**ked a taxi. / I was in such a bad m**oo**d.   ☐
4 There was a train str**i**ke that day. / It was qu**i**eter in the autumn.   ☐
5 My n**eigh**bour offered to take us. / I was so rel**ie**ved to get home.   ☐
6 The bus s**er**vice was terrible. / The j**ou**rney was a nightmare.   ☐

B 🔊 3.2 Listen and check. Practice saying the sentences.

GRAMMAR Present perfect questions

Complete the questions with the correct form of the verbs in brackets. Then choose the correct words in the answers.

1 A: .... you ever .... the pyramids? (see)
   B: No, never. *I love / I'd love to*, though.
2 A: .... you ever .... on holiday by yourself? (go)
   B: No, I've *ever / never* really fancied it.
3 A: .... you ever .... camping? (try)
   B: Yes, *lots / several times*.
4 A: .... you ever .... Japanese food? (eat)
   B: No, never. It's supposed *be / to be* delicious.
5 A: .... you ever .... a camel? (ride)
   B: No, never. *Have you? / Did you?* I've heard it's quite difficult.
6 A: .... you ever .... Disneyland with your kids? (visit)
   B: Yes, but I wouldn't go there if I were you. It's not worth *it / of it*.
7 A: .... you ever .... in a helicopter? (fly)
   B: No, never. What *does / is* it like?
8 A: .... you ever .... to Singapore? (go)
   B: Yes, it's wonderful. You should *to go / go*.

READING

A Read the webpage quickly and match the headings to the paragraphs. There is one heading that you don't need.

a But is it safe?
b How much does it cost?
c How long do people stay?
d Who are these couch-surfers?
e So what is couch-surfing, exactly?
f What are the disadvantages?
g What are the benefits?

B Complete the sentences with the words and phrases in **bold** in the webpage.

1 Ask Anna and Paolo for advice about Rome. They know the city ....
2 I don't mind where we go for the weekend. .... you.
3 Don't .... when you go to see grandma and granddad. Come home after a couple of hours.
4 It was .... when I first met my mother-in-law. I didn't speak Spanish and she didn't speak English.
5 I looked at the reviews of a lot of holiday companies. Adventure Tours have ....
6 My teachers were so helpful that I decided to .... at the end of the course.

Love to travel but hate paying for hotels? Too old for a youth hostel?

Then couch-surfing might be right up your street. Check out these FAQs:

1 .....e.....
Couch-surfing is a network of people who offer accommodation to strangers travelling in their area. It's simple. When you 'surf a couch' you are a guest in someone's house and they are your host. You don't pay for the room or couch, and your hosts will get the same favour back when they travel. They may stay with you or with another person in the network.

2 ....
Of course, there are smaller numbers of surfers in remote locations, but the network covers every continent (including Antarctica!) The top five couch-surfing nations are the United States, Germany, France, Canada and the United Kingdom. The average surfer is 27 years old and just over half the surfers are male.

3 ....
Couch-surfing was created so that everyone can travel the world and make meaningful connections, but staying with your host is always free. Many surfers like to take their hosts a gift or **treat them to a meal** to say thank you. They also thank people in small ways like doing the washing-up or sending a postcard from their next destination.

4 ....
Surfers get the advantage of staying with someone who knows the area **like the back of their hand**. They can tell how not to get ripped off, or what to do when it's pouring with rain. And when people of different cultures meet, who better than a local to help with social skills? Knowing whether to shake hands, bow, or kiss a person on the cheek can be very confusing!

5 ....
It's entirely up to the host. Some surfers come for a single night, or even just for dinner. The important thing is not to **outstay your welcome**, so surfers usually check with the host first. In the words of one host, 'We want surfers to be comfortable, but not too comfortable. Staying two or three nights is cool; longer gets a **bit awkward**.' And remember that in Germany they say 'Guests are like fish – after three days they start to smell ...'

6 ....
Well, there are always risks in life, but the majority of surfers never have any problems. Most travel networking sites have their own security systems. Hosts and surfers have to be registered and prove that they are who they say they are. There are reviews posted on the Internet and so surfers can select hosts with **a good track record**. Mostly, it's a question of common sense and avoiding anyone who sounds odd.

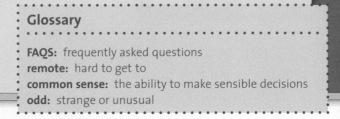

> **Glossary**
>
> **FAQS:** frequently asked questions
> **remote:** hard to get to
> **common sense:** the ability to make sensible decisions
> **odd:** strange or unusual

VOCABULARY Weather

A Write the words and phrase that describe temperature in the correct place on the diagram.

| freezing | cold | boiling hot | a bit chilly |
| quite warm | hot | | |

freezing

```
|———————|———————|———————|———————|———————|
0°C                                    100°C
```

B Replace the <u>underlined</u> words in the conversations with the words in the box.

| wet | pour down | drop | heat | reached |
| clear up | keep out of | humid | | |

1 A: Have you heard the weather forecast?
   B: Yes, apparently it's going to <u>rain a lot</u> all weekend.
   A: Oh, no, what a pain. I was thinking of going to the beach.
   B: I'd stay at home if I were you and <u>avoid</u> the rain.

2 A: What's the forecast for the weekend?
   B: Er, Saturday morning is supposed to be <u>rainy</u>, but then it should <u>improve</u> in the afternoon.
   A: Phew! That's a relief. I'm going to a wedding at 2:30.

3 A: I can't stand this <u>hot weather</u>.
   B: I know what you mean. The air conditioning isn't working in my office. The temperature <u>went up to</u> 40° yesterday.
   A: Poor you! It's so <u>hot and wet</u> that I can't sleep.
   B: Yeah, we need a storm to clear the air.

4 A: What are you up to at the weekend?
   B: It depends on the weather.
   A: Apparently, it's going to be freezing. They say it could <u>fall</u> to minus 5°.
   B: Time to stay in with a good book, I think.

Language note weather adjectives

- -

When describing the weather, we often use adjectives in pairs.
*It's going to be **cold** and **windy**.*
*The weather on holiday was **hot** and **humid**.*

GRAMMAR The future

A Rewrite the sentences with the words in brackets.

1 We will definitely be away in June. (going)
   We're going to be away in June.

2 Perhaps I'll try couch-surfing this year. (might)
   I ....

3 I can't meet up this weekend. I have to revise for my exams. (got) I ....

4 Jim might go travelling this summer. (thinking)
   Jim ....

5 I think it will be too cold for swimming. (probably)
   It ....

6 They definitely won't be on holiday in July. (going)
   They ....

B Use the words in 1–7 to complete the students' replies to the teacher's question.

1 *I've got to study for my university entrance exam.*
   (I / got / study for / my university entrance exam)

2 I'm not sure yet but
   ....
   (my friends and I / think / go / camping / near the coast)

3 ....
   (Marek and I / go to / a concert / in Manchester on Friday) We need to leave class early to get the train.

4 I'm not sure.
   ....
   (I / might / meet up with some friends in London)

5 ....
   (I / got / a free weekend) I'm going to catch up on some sleep.

6 ....
   (my sister and I / not go / be around) We've been invited to a party in Brighton.

7 I haven't made any plans but
   ....
   (I / probably / go to / my friend's barbecue)

What are you doing at the weekend?

C Circle the correct forms in *italics*.

1 A: Where *are you going / do you go* on holiday this year?

   B: I'm not sure. In fact I *will / might* not go away at all because I'm a bit short of money. My dad lent me some cash for a car and *I've got / I must* to pay him back. How about you? What are your plans?

   A: Well, it depends on the weather. I've only *got / got to* a week's holiday, so I want to go when it's hot and sunny.

   B: They say *it'll / it might* probably be another very hot summer, so you should be OK.

2 A: It's my day off today and *I'll have / I'm having* lunch with James and Gary in that new restaurant. Would you like to join us?

   B: I'd love to but I can't. I'm *going / thinking of going* to the doctor's.

   A: Oh, nothing serious, I hope.

   B: No, I'm fine, thanks. But *it'll probably take / it's taking* ages. The waiting room is always so crowded.

3 A: I've booked an apartment in Barcelona this year. *We might go / We're going* for two weeks in August. Do you fancy coming with us?

   B: It's nice of you to ask me but I'm not *going / thinking* to be here in the summer. *I'll spend / I'm spending* two months in Australia.

   A: Really? That sounds exciting.

   B: Yes, I'm thinking *to emigrate / of emigrating* there at some point.

   A: Wow, that's great.

Vocabulary Builder Quiz 3 (*OVB* pp10–12)

Try the *OVB* quiz for Unit 3. Write your answers in your notebook. Then check them and record your score.

A Find words that are both nouns and verbs to complete these sentences.

1 How much do they .... for a hotel room in the city centre. They let me use the car park free of ....

2 Was there much .... to your car in the accident? The bad publicity will .... his career in politics.

3 There has been a .... in petrol prices since the beginning of the year. It's so hot – I wish the temperature would ....

4 People often .... being good-looking with being successful. I don't understand the .... between lack of money and poor school results.

5 The government is going to .... the question of immigration. There was a heated .... in the town about knocking down the old church.

6 They .... diamonds in parts of Africa. My grandfather used to work in a coal ....

B Complete the verbs that begin with *re...* . Sometimes more than one verb is possible.

1 The gardens are closed for the winter. They will re............. in February.

2 We need to raise money to re............. the theatre roof.

3 I've applied for several jobs but I've been re............. every time.

4 I can't make the meeting on Friday so can we re............. a time?

5 I failed my driving test but I re............. it and I passed the second time.

6 This design won't work, so we'll need to re............. it.

7 I missed the last five minutes of the DVD. Can you re............. it?

C Match 1–6 and a–f to form compound nouns.

1	hand	a	jam
2	trade	b	union
3	tour	c	forecast
4	shopping	d	luggage
5	traffic	e	guide
6	weather	f	district

D Read the statements. Was each experience positive (✓) or negative (✗)?

1 It was a real bargain. The shop was closing down. ☐

2 It was a nightmare. It poured down all week. ☐

3 It was a total rip-off. There was hardly any food on the plate. ☐

4 It was well worth it. Give it a go some time. ☐

5 It was spoiled by the atmosphere between some of the guests. ☐

6 It was all cleared up really quickly. ☐

Score ___ /25

Wait a couple of weeks and try the quiz again. Compare your scores.

VOCABULARY Evening and weekend activities

A Complete the spidergram with the words in the box.

a bar to watch the sport	football	the cinema	clubbing	rollerblading	~~on the computer~~
walking in the country	cycling	golf	a swim	tennis	a ride on my bike
a friend's house for dinner	a run	a meal	the gym	shopping	

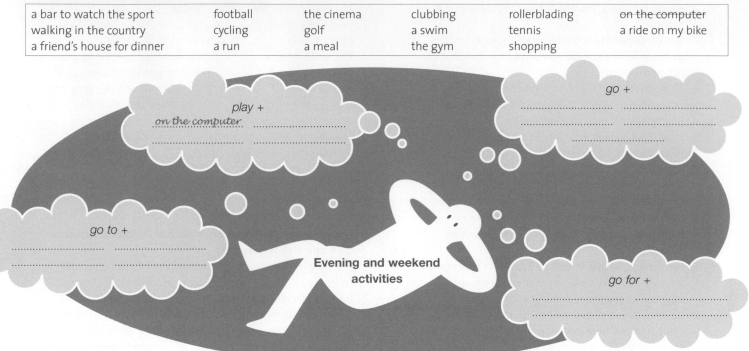

play +
on the computer ....
....

go +
....
....
....

go to +
....
....

Evening and weekend activities

go for +
....
....

B Complete the conversations. Put the words in brackets in the correct order.

1 A: Mum, I'm bored.
    B: Well, go and .... or ....
       (play / ride / your / football / bike)
    A: But that's boring. I do that every day.
    B: Well, ... and .... then.
       (in / bedroom / stay / tidy / up / your)

2 A: What did you do at the weekend?
    B: I just .... and ....
       (in / it / stayed / took / easy)
    A: How come? You're usually such a party animal.
    B: Yeah, I .... (fancy / just / going / clubbing / didn't)
    A: Fair enough.

3 A: What's your idea of a perfect Friday night?
    B: Going .... or just .... at home. What about you?
       (easy / for / to / it / house / a / friend's / dinner / taking)
    A: My idea of heaven is ....
       (for / and / staying / exams / studying / in / my)
    B: Why on earth would you want to do that?
    A: Only joking. My ideal night out is going .... and then ....
       (going / watch / clubbing / bar / football / to / a / the / to)

GRAMMAR Frequency (present and past)

A Complete the questions with the answers. Use the present simple of the verbs in the box.

play golf	go walking in the country	eat out
go clubbing	go to the gym	work

1 A: How .... ?
    B: About once every two months. The local restaurants are quite expensive.

2 A: .... ever .... weekends?
    B: Yes, all the time. I'm at my desk every Sunday morning.

3 A: .... much?
    B: Not as much as I should, so I'm starting to put on weight.

4 A: .... ever .... ?
    B: No, never. It's not my kind of thing. I'm into team sports like football or rugby.

5 A: .... a lot?
    B: Yeah, at least three times a week. My best friend is a DJ.

6 A: .... often .... ?
    B: Whenever I can. I love being away from the city.

B Look at the answers to the question 'How often do you listen to music?' Choose the correct words. Then number the answers in order (1 = most often).

a Not *quite / that* often. Maybe once a week.   ......
b *All the / Every* time. I can't live without my iPod.   ..1..
c Hardly *ever / never*. I never have the time.   ......
d Not as much as I *used to / was used to*. Maybe only once a fortnight.   ......
e *Never / Not never*. I'm more into books.   ......
f Quite *much / often*. Probably five times a week.   ......
g Not as much as I *would / did* like to. Just two or three times a week.   ......
h Nearly *every / all* day. Usually when I want to relax in the evenings.   ......

C If possible, replace the <u>underlined</u> past simple forms with *used to*. One sentence cannot change.

1 When I was at my first school, I <u>had</u> loads of time to see my friends, but now I have to study all week.
2 I <u>took</u> every weekend off, but these days I spend every waking hour at the office.
3 I <u>worked</u> from six in the morning until 10 at night one day last week. It was just exhausting.
4 My colleagues and I always <u>left</u> work on time but now we're expected to stay late at the office.
5 I <u>spent</u> all weekend with my family before I started working. Now, I hardly ever see them.

LISTENING

A ◐ 4.1 You are going to hear Mike giving a talk about making small changes to your life. Listen to Part 1 and circle the four aspects that he mentions.

travel   sport   food   relationships   free time   shopping

B ◐ 4.2 Listen to Part 2. Mike, Amy, and Jack talk about the changes they made. Who did or said what? Write M, A, or J.

Changing my routine has changed my attitude.   ..A..
I became bored with my hobby even though I'm quite good at it.   ......
I thought you needed money to have a good time.   ......
It's silly to keep repeating things that upset you.   ......
I wanted to share my ideas with other people.   ......
I feel motivated to help others join in.   ......
I developed a great social life at no cost.   ......

PRONUNCIATION Sentence stress

Language note unstressed sounds

Structural words (e.g. prepositions, conjunctions, auxiliaries and articles) are not usually stressed because they don't carry the main information in a sentence. The unstressed syllables are usually pronounced with the same vowel sound, /ə/.

Like ə a lot of peəople, I used to have a pretty fixed routine ...

A Mark the stresses in these sentences from *Listening*. Practise saying the sentences with the correct stressed and unstressed syllables.

1 Like a lot of people, I used to have a pretty fixed routine.
2 I'm in a much better mood when I get to work.
3 I'm into sport and I'm quite good at it.
4 All my friends were playing the same sports.
5 What have you got to lose?

B ◐ 4.3 Listen and check. Practice the sentences again.

DEVELOPING CONVERSATIONS
Are you any good?

Complete the replies with the phrases in the box.

Yeah, quite good.	No, I'm useless.
I'm OK.	No, not really.

So are you any good at singing?

1 .... I can't sing at all. In fact they asked me leave the school choir.
2 .... Actually, I've been in a band for ages and we've won a few talent competitions.
3 .... I used to sing a bit at school and I like to do karaoke with my friends.
4 .... I haven't got a very good voice. I get really embarrassed if people hear me sing.

VOCABULARY Problems and sports

Look at the cartoon and complete the words for the sports problems.

1 A: What's up with you?
   B: I'm not making excuses but my shoulders are really
      s _ _ _ _ . I don't think I can play in goal today.
2 A: Is something wrong with you as well?
   B: Er ... yes, coach. Can I be substitute today? I've
      p _ _ _ _ _ a thigh muscle and I don't think I can play
      the full 90 minutes.
3 A: What happened to you?
   B: I f _ _ _ off my horse and b _ _ _ _ my arm. I'm going
      to be in plaster for six weeks.

4 A: How come the referee has got a b _ _ _ _ _ nose?
   B: Max just tried a shot at goal but he missed and hit him
      in the face.
5 A: What happened to Phil?
   B: He just slipped and b _ _ _ _ _ his head on the goalpost. I
      hope he'll be OK.
6 A: Have you seen the other team? They look so fit.
   B: I know. I'm sure they're going to b _ _ _ us.
7 A: Are you OK?
   B: I think I need to stop. I haven't been for a run for ages. I'm
      so u _ _ _ _ .

GRAMMAR Duration

A Match the question halves. Then match the questions (1–5) to the answers (a–e).

1 How long did ⌐ Jodie been doing ballet?   ......
2 How long has ⌐ you in plaster after your accident?   ......
3 How long were ⌐ you train before the marathon?   *d*
4 How long was   you been doing yoga?   ......
5 How long have   your team in the first division?   ......

a For just one season. We were beaten so many times we
   went back down again.
b For about six weeks. It's still quite painful.
c For just a few months. It's very relaxing and I feel better
   for it.
d For about six months. I ran four times a week.
e For years off and on. She started when she was just four.

B Find and correct a tense mistake and a time expression mistake in each conversation.

1 A: I have riding lessons since last summer. *I've been having*
   B: Really? I fell off a horse when I was a kid and I've been
      a bit scared from since. *since then*
2 A: Kim was telling me you've taken up the piano. How
      long have you played?
   B: Just a few months. I practise every day during an hour.
3 A: We used to do judo at my old school.
   B: Really? That's unusual. How long have you done that
      for?
   A: For the age of about 14 until I left.
4 A: You've got a great voice.
   B: Thanks. From quite recently, I was a singing teacher but
      I had to give it up.
   A: That's amazing. How long have you taught for?
   B: Six years off and on.

DEVELOPING WRITING An email – asking for information

A Read the email at the bottom of the page. Tick the correct statements.
a It's the first time Richard has written to the organisation. ☐
b He has never been part of a conservation group before. ☐
c He wants to find out about a job. ☐
d He asks for information about transport. ☐
e He asks about equipment. ☐
f He says how he found out about the group. ☐

B Complete the email with the words in the box.

grateful	provided	let	keen	regards
advert	join	experience	confirm	forward

Language note indirect questions

We often use indirect questions in writing to sound polite. They
- use statement word order
- don't use *do / does / did*
- use *if / whether* when there isn't a question word
- often use introductory phrases like:
  I would like to know ...

C Underline the indirect questions in the email.

D Make indirect questions using the introductory phrases.
1 Do I have to wear anything special?
  Can you confirm .... ?
2 How is transport to each session organised?
  I would like to know ....
3 Where is the nearest car park to the gym?
  Can you confirm .... ?
4 Does the tutor have a good success rate?
  Could you tell me .... ?
5 How much does a course of lessons cost?
  I'd be grateful if you could tell me ....
6 Will I have to take an exam or a test?
  I would like to know ....

E Write an email (120–150 words) to ask for information about an activity that you would like to do. Use an idea from the list or your own idea. Follow the content checklist and remember to use indirect questions.
- a course at a college or with a one-to-one tutor
- a sport / activity at a gym
- joining a volunteering group

Checklist
- how you heard about the course / activity / group
- the days and times
- the cost
- if you need any experience / skills
- if you need any equipment

Learner tip

If you write to someone you don't know to ask for information, don't include too many questions. If you keep the number of requests fairly short, you are more likely to get a quick reply!

Dear Sir / Madam

I have recently moved into the area and I saw an ¹................................. for your volunteering group in the local library. I am ²................................. to find out more about your organisation.

I have always been interested in local history and geography, but I have never done any conservation work. Could you tell me whether any ³................................. or special skills are necessary to ⁴................................. the group? I would also like to know whether volunteers need to bring their own tools, or whether these will be ⁵................................. .

Could you ⁶................................. the days and times that the group meets? I would also be ⁷................................. if you could ⁸................................. me know whereabouts the group works and the type of tasks the volunteers do.

Finally, could you tell me if you organise any special courses in conservation?

I look ⁹................................. to hearing from you soon.

Kind ¹⁰.................................

Richard Clarke

DEVELOPING CONVERSATIONS
Music, films and books

Circle the correct words to complete the conversation.

A: Do you watch films [1] *much / lot*?

B: Yeah, all the time.

A: What [2] *like / kind* of films are you into?

B: [3] *All / Every* sorts really, but [4] *hardly / mainly* science fiction and adventure movies.

A: Oh right. Any films [5] *of / in* particular?

B: I don't know ... *Blade Runner, The Matrix* series, [6] *stuffs / stuff* like that.

A: So have you seen [7] *anything / any* good recently?

B: Well, I saw this old black and white movie from the 1950s called *Invasion of the Body Snatchers*.

VOCABULARY Music

Complete the conversations with the pairs of adjectives in the box.

> catchy / repetitive   bland / commercial
> depressing / uplifting   heavy / soft
> moving / sentimental

1 A: Do you mind if we don't listen to this song? I find it really .... It kind of reminds me of when my dad died.

   B: Sure, no problem, I'll put on something more ....

2 A: Oh, turn the radio off. That DJ is so boring. He just plays this .... music the whole time.

   B: Well, they need to play .... stuff sometimes. They need to make money.

3 A: I love the lyrics of this song. They're so .... and romantic.

   B: Don't tell me you're going to cry. I can't believe you like this .... rubbish.

4 A: Please stop humming that tune to yourself. You're driving me mad.

   B: Sorry, but it's just so .... And the beat is so ...., I can't get it out of my head.

5 A: Are you into rock music?

   B: No, it doesn't do much for me. It's a bit .... I like something .... and relaxing – a nice bit of Vivaldi or Debussy.

READING

A Read the article quickly. What is the main reason for writing it?

a to criticise teenagers who download illegally

b to give some facts about the problem of illegal downloads

c a describe how to file share

B Read the text again. Number the paragraph summaries in order.

the extent of the problem ......

possible solutions for the future ......

examples of people who have been punished ......

the ways people get music ......

C Look at the bold words in the article. What do they refer to?

one or two = .CDs.

D What do these numbers in the article refer to?

£1 billion (line 13)	14–24 (line 17)	10 000 (line 19)
48 per cent (line 21)	$222 000 (line 29)	1 702 (line 31)

The changing face of music

Until quite recently people were happy to go along to a music shop, look through the CDs and maybe buy **one or two**. But since the development of the Internet, the music scene is unrecognisable from what it was. Nowadays, music can be downloaded from the Internet to a computer
5 or mobile phone. Most people do this legally, by buying songs from businesses like iTunes, but there is also the growing problem of file-sharing. **This** is downloading songs to a computer but also allowing other people to copy them.

Although file-sharing is in itself a legal technology,
10 many people use **it** to exchange copyrighted materials without permission. This is often referred to as 'music piracy'. It is estimated that **this** will cost the recording industry up to £1 billion over the next few years. A recent survey has found that teenagers and
15 students have an average of 842 illegal downloads on their iPod or digital music player. The research also showed that half of 14–24-year-olds are happy to share all the music on their hard drive. This would allow others to copy up to 10 000 songs at
20 any one time. The average digital music player holds 1 770 songs meaning that 48 per cent of a music collection is copied illegally.

However, the music industry has been fighting back. Organisations that represent musicians
25 have taken legal action against thousands of people across the world for music piracy. **One of them** is a thirty-year-old woman from Minnesota in the USA. Jamie Thomas was asked

E **Complete the sentences with the words and phrases in the box. All of them appeared in the article.**

| the research also showed | a recent survey |
| it is estimate | nowadays | the average |

1 .... into local transport has shown that car use has declined after the rise in petrol costs. .... a slow-down in car sales.

2 .... age of the students on the course was 17.

3 .... , couples are getting married later or deciding not to marry at all.

4 .... that temperatures will rise by two degrees in the next 20 years.

30 to pay $222 000 for the songs she had downloaded and distributed without permission. This was estimated at a total of 1 702.

So, what is the way forward? UK Internet providers and the record industry have come to a new agreement to stop illegal downloaders. **They**
35 plan to block their access to download sites or to slow down their Internet connection to make downloads impractical. **Another possibility** is to get downloaders to pay a subscription for access to legal music files. The positive message is that **80**
40 **per cent of them** said they would be willing to pay for a legal service.

Vocabulary Builder Quiz 4 (*OVB* pp14–16)

Try the *OVB* quiz for Unit 4. Write your answers in your notebook. Then check them and record your score.

A Which is the odd one out in each set?

1	net	helmet	defender	weights
2	kick	fit	score	shoot
3	warm-up	bloody	plaster	stiff
4	tournament	semi-final	season	quarter-final
5	balance	strength	technique	course

B Complete the adjectives that begin with *un...* .

1 I haven't done any exercise for years. I'm so un..............

2 She isn't very well so it's un............. she'll come to the party.

3 They blamed me for the team's mistakes. It was so un

4 We hadn't seen her for years so her phone call was completely un..............

5 He's so un.............. He never keeps his promises.

6 Everyone nearly fell asleep. He was a very un............. speaker.

7 I'm afraid your job application has been un..............

8 I need to think about it. I'm un............. about what to do.

C Match the sentence halves.

1 I'm not very sporty but my boss persuaded me	a advantage of every opportunity.
2 You need to try to take	b on very well in the second half.
3 If you don't warm up, you might pull	c impossible challenges.
4 If you missed the match, you can download	d to join the team.
5 We weren't bad in the first half but we didn't get	e a muscle or get stiff legs.
6 Our coach always sets us	f it from the Internet and watch it later.

D What form of the words in brackets do you need to complete the text?

I usually play football about three times a week. I play in [1] (defend) and I guess I'm not bad. The team's level of [2] (fit) is quite high because our [3] (train) sessions are pretty [4] (challenge). Last week I ended up with an [5] (injure) to my ankle, but it was nothing to do with the match. The pitch was really [6] (slip) and as we were heading back to the changing rooms, I twisted my ankle and fell backwards. It was so embarrassing.

Score ___/25

Wait a couple of weeks and try the quiz again. Compare your scores.

Glossary

copyrighted: protected by law so that the copyright owner has control over how a work is used

Internet provider: a company that connects people to the Internet

subscription: an agreement to pay money regularly for a service you receive

05 WORKING LIFE

VOCABULARY Jobs

A Complete the job names.

1 **Public sector**
   ci _v_ il s _e_ rv _a_ _n_ t

2 **Construction**
   pl _ _ _ e _
   l _ _ o _ r _ _ r
   e _ _ _ tr _ c _ _ _ _

3 **IT, technical**
   p _ _ _ _ r _ m _ _ _
   en _ i _ _ er

4 **Legal, finance**
   l _ w _ _ _ _
   ac _ _ _ _ _ t _ _ _

5 **Art, design, new media**
   gr _ _ _ ic
   d _ _ _ _ _ n _ r

6 **Healthcare**
   s _ r _ _ _ _ n

7 **Property**
   e _ t _ _ e _ ge _ _
   s _ c _ r _ t _ _ g _ _ r _

B Mark the main stress on the words in exercise A.
civil <u>ser</u>vant

> **Learner tip**
>
> Remember to record pronunciation in your vocabulary notebook, e.g. main stress, silent letters and phonetics for words with difficult pronunciation.

C Match the sentence halves.

1 It's not a bad job. I'm involved ......
2 I feel so fed up. I've applied ......
3 I've worked late every night this week. I've got ......
4 People often ask how I got ......
5 I know all jobs have their ......
6 It's such a relief to work shorter hours. In my old job I did ......
7 In the interview they asked if I could work under ......

a pressure. Of course I said yes.
b for hundreds of jobs but no luck yet.
c an important deadline to meet.
d boring moments, but I expected computing to be more fun than this.
e in inspecting hotels for a travel company.
f something like 50 hours a week.
g into the film industry. I worked my way up from the bottom.

D Complete the opinions below with the pairs of words in the box. Which of the jobs in exercise A are the people talking about?

insecure / physically demanding	
responsibility / paperwork	creative / varied
stressful / rewarding	well paid / competitive

1 Of course, it's .... because you have people's lives in your hands, but it's also incredibly .... when someone's health improves.
2 We work on short contracts so it's quite .... It's also .... – I spend the day lifting and carrying heavy weights.
3 It's hard coming up with new ideas all the time, but, after all, people pay me to be .... I'm self-employed and I have a wide range of clients, so my work is very ....
4 People think that because we deal with money that we are very .... You can earn a lot but only really in the top jobs and they are difficult to find. It's a very .... industry.
5 It's a big .... when we have to prepare a case for court, but one of the worst things is the .... Working with each client involves hundreds of documents, letters and emails.

VOCABULARY
Work places and activities

A Find and correct two mistakes in each example.

1 I'm in the sales. I'm the rep of the north-west.
2 I'm the warehouse manager. I deal with prepare the orders for delivery and all the admins.
3 I work in the account department. I'm responsibility for all the staff salaries.
4 I work in human research. I'm involved of recruitment.
5 I make part of the marketing team. I'm responsible of a big campaign for our new mobile phones.

B What do the underlined words stand for? Use a dictionary if necessary.

1 We need a new sales <u>rep</u>. Tell <u>HR</u> to prepare an <u>ad</u>.
2 I have a <u>CV</u> here from a good candidate. Please pass to the <u>MD</u> for her to look at.
3 I work in <u>PR</u>. I have a <u>PA</u> to help me with <u>admin</u>, which is great.
4 I work in <u>R&D</u>, but I'd like to get into <u>IT</u>. The problem is it's quite competitive.

Language note *work* + preposition

work in + place / area of work, e.g. I *work in a factory*. / Kim *works in publishing*.
work for + name of company, e.g. I'd like to *work for Vodafone*.
work as + job, e.g. How long *have you worked as a teacher*?
work on + a project, e.g. We*'ve been working on a new design*.
work with + person / equipment, e.g. *Did you work with* Leo on the sales figures? / We *have to work with dangerous chemicals*.

DEVELOPING CONVERSATIONS

That must be ...

Write responses using the adjectives in the box.

disappointing	stressful	tiring	fascinating	rewarding	fun

1 A: I have such a lot on my plate – recruitment, contracts, training and all the admin.
   B: *That must be stressful.*

2 A: I work with children with learning difficulties. It's amazing to see the progress they can make.
   B: ....

3 A: I really thought I was going to get my promotion, but my boss said maybe next year.
   B: ....

4 A: I work such long hours and I never take my full holiday entitlement.
   B: ....

5 A: I'm the head of research into the use of robots in medicine.
   B: ....

6 A: Basically, my hobby has become my job. I design computer games.
   B: ....

LISTENING

🔊 **5.1 You are going to hear five people talking about unsuccessful job interviews. Match the speakers (1-5) to the letters (a–e).**
Who ...
a didn't appear serious enough?
b criticised his / her current boss?
c came across as too big-headed?
d arrived late?
e didn't do enough preparation?

Speaker 1 ......
Speaker 2 ......
Speaker 3 ......
Speaker 4 ......
Speaker 5 ......

PRONUNCIATION

Past simple *-ed* endings

A **Look at these extracts from *Listening*. How many syllables does each past simple form have?**
1 he invited a group of us to go for a meal .....3.....
2 when I looked at my watch, I couldn't believe it was 11:30 ......
3 My alarm went off at 6:30 but I just ignored it and went back to sleep. ......
4 Every time the interviewer asked me something, my mind just went blank. ......
5 It sounded really good, so I decided to go for it. ......
6 I remembered I'd skipped breakfast. ......
7 The head of sales looked a bit surprised but handed them both over. ......
8 I answered it because it was one of my co-workers. ......

B **Mark the links in the sentences in exercise A.**
1 He invited a group of us to go for a meal.

C 🔊 **5.2 Listen and check your answers.**

GRAMMAR
Have to, don't have to, can

A Make these sentences sound more natural. Use *have to*, *don't have to*, or *can*.

1 It's necessary for us to do a minimum of 35 hours a week. (We ... .)
   We have to work a minimum of 35 hours a week

2 It isn't possible for you to book time off at short notice. (You ... .)

3 It's necessary for me to put my staff under pressure to meet deadlines. (I ... .)

4 It's possible for us to work from home at least one day a week. (We ... .)

5 It isn't necessary for managers to wear a suit unless they are meeting clients.(Managers ... .)

6 It's possible for the staff to take 25 days' holiday a year. (The staff ... .)

7 It isn't necessary for the security guard to check people's bags. (The security guard ... .)

B Look at the answers (B) below. Write questions for the answers using the words in brackets.

1 A: *What time do you have to get up for work?*
   (you / have / get up for work?)
   B: About 5 a:m. to be at work for 6.

2 A: ....
   (we / can / work flexi-time?)
   B: No, everyone has to do the same hours, 9 to 5.

3 A: ....
   (Rob / have to / work?)
   B: He does something like 50 or 60 hours at the hospital.

4 A: ....
   (Lisa / can / work from home?)
   B: No, the boss likes to have everyone at the office in case there's a problem.

5 A: ....
   (the reps / have to / travel every year?)
   B: Thousands of kilometres across ten countries. It's very stressful.

6 A: ....
   (the staff / can / use computers to send personal emails?)
   B: Yes, but not too often. Everyone is supposed to be working.

7 A: ....
   (you / have to / work weekends?)
   B: Yeah, we do. Usually about once a month.

C It's Katie's first day in her job at a law firm. She's talking to Nicole, the head of HR. Choose the correct forms.

N: Morning, Katie. Oh, I see that you're wearing trousers and a top. Actually, we have a strict dress code here. All the lawyers [1] *have to / don't have to* wear suits.

K: I'm sorry, no-one told me, and in my old job we [2] *can / could* wear whatever we wanted.

N: Not here, I'm afraid. Until recently, women [3] *could / couldn't* wear trousers at all. Another thing you should know: computers are for professional use, so you [4] *can't / don't have to* use your PC to send personal emails or to surf the Net.

K: Of course. What about time off? In my last job, I [5] *had to / have to* give a month's notice before I [6] *could / couldn't* take holiday.

N: Yes, it's the same here. And you [7] *have to / don't have to* fill in a form and get it signed by your manager and by me.

K: OK, and what about breaking for lunch?

N: Most people take a break for an hour between 12 and 2. You decide when you want to go for lunch, you [8] *can't / don't have to* check with your manager. Oh, one more thing – ID cards. Everyone [9] *has to / have to* wear their card at all times.

K: OK, thanks. I hope I remember. In my last job, we [10] *couldn't / didn't have to* wear ID cards, but it was a much smaller firm.

GRAMMAR Talking about rules

A Complete the sentences with the pairs of verbs in the box.

should / turn off	~~not allow / drink~~	shouldn't / send
not suppose / leave	suppose / clear	allow / buy

1 Employees *are not allowed to drink* alcohol or smoke anywhere in the building.

2 We .... company products at a 10 per cent discount off the normal price.

3 All employees .... their tables when they have finished lunch.

4 I .... really .... personal mail from the post room, but it's OK just this once.

5 Visitors .... the building without signing out and returning their passes.

6 We .... really .... our computers at the end of each day, but sometimes I'm in a rush, so I leave mine on.

B Read the list of some of the world's strangest rules. Find and correct a mistake in each example.

1 You are not allowed die in the Houses of Parliament in London.

2 You are not suppose to put a stamp showing the British king or queen's head upside-down on an envelope.

3 In Scotland, if someone knocks on your door and asks to use your toilet, you have let them come in.

4 In Ohio, you don't allowed to get a fish drunk.

5 In Florida, single women no are supposed to parachute on Sundays.

6 In Vermont, a woman have to get written permission from her husband to wear false teeth.

7 In Milan, you have smile at all times, except during funerals or hospital visits.

8 In France, you no allowed to name a pig 'Napoleon'.

READING

A Read the article quickly. Write the missing headings in the correct place.

Be accurate	Give the full story	Be honest
Be concise	Send a covering letter	

B Read the article again. Decide if these sentences are true or false, or if the article doesn't say.

1 People in recruitment don't spend long reading each CV.
2 An employer never reads a CV that is longer than two pages.
3 You should put information about your oldest job first.
4 It's essential to give information about every job you have done.
5 Employers hardly ever check information in a CV.
6 You shouldn't send CVs with the same content to a range of employers.
7 An employer won't read a CV without a covering letter.

C Replace the underlined words in these sentences with the phrases in bold in the article.

1 Sending your CV to a recruitment website can give you more opportunities of getting a job.
2 A website with clear headings makes the key information easy to see.
3 If you go into a lot of detail about every job you've ever done, it is boring for the reader.
4 I don't have a problem with interviews. The hard part is gaining a first introduction to the company.
5 You want to make a good impression but it's madness to not be completely honest on your CV. If they catch you out, you won't even get an interview.

TIPS FOR A BETTER CV!

A good curriculum vitae (CV), with information about you and your qualifications and experience, will **boost your chances** of getting an interview for a job, but a poor CV could ruin everything before you even start. On average, a recruiter will spend just 15 to 20 seconds reviewing a CV, so it's important to get it right.

✔ ....

Remember that your CV is only a way of **getting your foot in the door**, so keep it short. Most successful CVs include the following sections: Profile, Achievements, Experience, Special skills (languages / computers), Education, Training, and Interests (this is optional). Use no more than two sides of A4 paper and save the real detail for your interview.

✔ Make it look good

Make sure the key points of your CV are clear. Use bullet points and relatively short sentences for the key information. Leaving a border of white space around the text also makes the information **stand out** and makes the CV easier to read.

✔ ....

Give information about your work history in date order. Start with the most recent job first and don't leave any gaps. If you have been out of work for a time, give reasons, but don't go into details about jobs you did more than 10 years ago.

✔ Include relevant facts, not lists

List your duties, achievements, and responsibilities under each job. Use a separate section in your CV for specific skills, such as languages, administrative or computing skills. There's no need to include them for every job you've done. This **makes dull reading** for the recruiter.

✔ ....

Although you want to present yourself well, don't **bend the truth**. You are likely to be caught out and your application rejected. Many companies employ people to check the facts that candidates supply, including qualifications.

✔ ....

Always check for errors. Use the spell-checker on your computer to deal with basic errors of spelling and grammar, but also get someone else to read your CV and tell you what they think.

✔ Adapt it

Take the time to adapt your CV for each job you apply for. Research the company and use the job advert to assess what they are looking for. Link your skills and experience to the requirements of each job. If you are sending your CV to a recruitment website, look at the jobs and employers on the site and adapt your CV accordingly.

✔ ....

Use this to highlight information from your CV that is most relevant to the job you are applying for. It isn't good practice to send your CV to an employer on its own without this.

Glossary

profile: the section of a CV with a summary of the person's key skills and what he / she can do for the employer
A4: a standard (210 x 297 mm) sheet of paper
bullet point: a printed circle before items in a list to make them clearer
gap: something that is missing

GRAMMAR *Be used to, get used to*

A Choose the correct ending (a or b) in speaker 2's answers below.

1 Speaker 1: How is everything at your new school?
  Speaker 2: Fine now, but …
  a it took a while to get used to it.
  b I'm getting used to it.

2 Speaker 1: How are things with the new baby?
  Speaker 2: Oh, she's wonderful, but we're exhausted! It's difficult to …
  a get used to waking up every few hours.
  b be used to waking up every few hours.

3 Speaker 1: Are you enjoying living in the country?
  Speaker 2: Yes, but it seems so quiet. Coming from London, we're …
  a getting used to it.
  b used to noise and traffic all day.

4 Speaker 1: What do think of Lucy's blonde hair?
  Speaker 2: Well, it was a shock at first, as she's always been dark, but …
  a I'm getting used to it.
  b I'm being used to it.

5 Speaker 1: Do you like boarding school? It must be hard being away from your family.
  Speaker 2: To be honest, I've always studied away from home, so …
  a I'll never get used to it.
  b I'm used to it.

6 Speaker 1: Is your arm OK now after you broke it?
  Speaker 2: No, not really. I can't play sport now, which is a real shame, but …
  a I'll just have to get used to it.
  b I'm used to it.

B A team of programmers have left the US to work for an IT company in Japan. Write suitable words to complete these extracts from their blog.

So, we've been here for a few weeks and things are going OK …

GREG: *It didn't take me long to* [1] *get used to* the job but the atmosphere in the office is very different – a lot more formal. I'm still [2] .... used to the different system of names (they don't use first names here so much).

NICO: *I'm not really used to* [3] .... a suit for the office. I've never had to do it before. But the job is fun and we're learning a lot.

MEL: *Meetings are so much more formal here. You sit in a specific place and you wait your turn to speak. I* [4] .... used to a lot more noise and jokes in the meetings we have back home.

KARA: *The food is great but I was used to* [5] .... sushi a lot back in the US. I'm having problems getting [6] .... to the journey in to work, though. The trains are just so crowded.

VICTOR: *Everyone bows here instead of shaking hands. I still haven't* [7] .... used to that, but I'll keep trying. But everything is so clean and well organised here – that's very easy to get used [8] ....

Posted at 6.02AM   LEAVE A COMMENT | BOOKMARK

DEVELOPING WRITING *More formal writing – a covering letter*

A Choose the correct information about writing more formal letters.

1 If you know the name of the person you are writing to, start the letter *Dear (name) / Hi (name)*.

2 If you don't know the name of the person you are writing to, start the letter *Dear Employers / Dear Sir or Madam*.

3 If you know the name of the person you are writing to, end the letter *Yours sincerely / Yours faithfully*.

4 If you don't know the name of the person you are writing to, end the letter *Yours sincerely / Yours faithfully*.

B Read Marcus's covering letter opposite. Which three things from the covering letter checklist did he not do?

1 ....
2 ....
3 ....

Covering letter checklist
- *Refer to a specific job with a job title and / or job reference.*
- *Say where you saw the job advertised.*
- *Confirm your contact details.*
- *Show that you have relevant qualifications.*
- *Show that you have relevant previous experience.*
- *Use a fairly formal tone, and accurate language.*
- *Use a formal greeting and sign off.*

C Where would you put the missing information to make Marcus's letter more complete?

1 ... for a Tourist Information Officer (reference IO1791)
2 I can be contacted on my mobile: 08614 308692, or at home on 01855 593410.
3 I have a degree in French and Spanish, and a diploma in Tourism Management. I also have knowledge of several computer programs, and am currently learning Italian.

Dear Sir or Madam,

I am writing in response to your job advertisement on the Jobsonline website. I am enclosing my CV for your consideration.

As you can see from my CV, I have five years' experience working in the tourist industry, both as a tour guide abroad and as an Information Officer in my hometown. I have experience in managing teams of employees, both in this country and abroad. In my current job, I have been in sole charge of my local Information Office for the last year.

I am available for interview at any time and please do not hesitate to contact me for further information.

I look forward to hearing from you.

Yours faithfully,
Marcus Ryder

D Underline the more formal ways of saying these things. Refer to both the letter and exercise C.

1 You can call me ...
2 I can use ...
3 I can meet you ...
4 Here's my CV for you to look at.
5 I've been the boss of ...
6 This letter is about ...
7 Hope to hear from you soon.

E A British company is expanding its links with tourism in your area and needs to take on English-speaking staff. Write a covering letter (120–150 words) to apply for one of these jobs:

- a full-time guide in the local museum.
- a part-time tour guide around the main tourist sites of your city.
- a full-time writer to provide information for your city's tourist website.

Vocabulary Builder Quiz 5 (OVB pp18–20)

Try the *OVB* quiz for Unit 5. Write your answers in your notebook. Then check them and record your score.

A Cross out the nouns that don't go with the adjectives.

1 competitive   industry / market / finances / atmosphere
2 demanding   bonus / children / boss / job
3 permanent   staff / delivery / contract / damage
4 rewarding   deadline / job / experience / opportunity
5 supportive   boss / colleagues / accounts / atmosphere
6 cramped   flat / conditions / training / office

B Find words that are both verbs and nouns to complete these sentences.

1 We need to do more market .... on this product. The marketing team is going to .... opportunities in the Far East.
2 I don't get much .... in this job. If you decide to leave your job, I will .... you.
3 We cannot put up with emotional .... in this company. Managers who .... younger members of staff will be disciplined.
4 All the office furniture was covered in .... Please ask the cleaners to .... my desk and chair.
5 I think you would be taking a .... to set up your own business now. I never complain because I don't want to .... losing my job.
6 The nurses are going to .... a pay rise. Every time I see my boss she makes a new .... on my time.

C Choose the correct words.

1 He started *swearing* / *abusing* at everyone in the meeting.
2 My basic salary isn't great but I earn quite a lot more in *wages* / *bonuses*.
3 Working in *finances* / *accounts* isn't very rewarding but at least it's secure.
5 I've just placed an *order* / *delivery* online for a new laptop.
6 We're going to be *responsible* / *involved* for setting up a new office in Milan.
7 How many hours are you *recruited* / *contracted* to work every month?

D Replace the underlined text with words from the box.

put up with	with more variety	do any lifting
handed in my notice	deadline	handle	put in charge of

1 I've just been made responsible for the whole sales team.
2 What's the last time and date for delivery of the order?
3 I hate my job. I want to do something that consists of lots of different things.
4 I've just told my boss I'm going to leave.
5 They don't tolerate any form of bullying in the workplace.
6 I couldn't work anywhere where you have to touch fresh meat.
7 I have a bad back, so I can't move heavy objects.

Score ___ /25

**Wait a couple of weeks and try the quiz again.
Compare your scores.**

VOCABULARY
Describing souvenirs and presents

A Find six materials in the word snake. Match them with the sets of objects (1–6).

claysilkleatherwoodenplasticsilver

1 .... sandals / belts / bags
2 .... masks / bowls / carving
3 .... rings / bracelets / necklaces
4 .... pots / pipes / bricks
5 .... scarves / ties / shirts
6 .... toys / models / bags

B Choose two of the three adjectives to complete the sentences. Write them in the correct order.

1 A: They've got some .... (hand-printed / lovely / hand-carved) paper in that shop. I think I'll buy some to wrap Mum's present.
   B: Nice idea. I've bought her a .... (little / nice / tacky) silver ring. Hope she likes it.

2 A: The local shop is supposed to sell .... (hand-made / cute / traditional) rugs. Shall we go and have a look?
   B: Actually, it's not worth it. They only have .... (horrible / gorgeous / machine-woven) stuff there. Let's try the market instead.

3 A: Look at these .... (hand-woven / hand-painted / gorgeous) plates. They would make really nice souvenirs.
   B: Oh, yes, much better than the .... (little / nice / tacky) plastic models they were selling at the hotel.

4 A: What did Millie bring you back from holiday?
   B: A lovely silver necklace for me and a .... (cute / carved / hand-woven) hat for my daughter. She looks so sweet in it.

> **Language note** order of adjectives
>
> When you use two or more adjectives together, 'opinion' adjectives usually go before 'fact' adjectives, e.g.
> a **beautiful** old Indian clay pot
> a **gorgeous** hand-carved wooden box

DEVELOPING CONVERSATIONS
Avoiding repetition

Make these sentences sound more natural. Change the wording to include *one* or *ones*.

1 Can I have a look at those gloves? The red ~~leather gloves~~ next to the black bag. _ones._
2 This belt is made of leather whereas that belt is made of plastic.
3 I'll take the large bottle of water unless you have any smaller bottles.
4 Don't you have any paper bags? I hate using plastic bags.
5 These machine-woven rugs are in the sale whereas those hand-woven rugs aren't.
6 I'm not sure which ring to choose. I like the gold ring but it's much more expensive than the silver ring.

LISTENING

A 🔊 **6.1 Listen to Jodie talking to her friend Emma about her holiday. Tick the things in the picture that Jodie and her husband bought.**

B Who was each present for? Match the people to the correct object.

Jodie	Eddie	Emma	Nick	Emma's children

PRONUNCIATION
Intonation on question tags

A Write the missing question tags.

1 You were away for about six weeks, _weren't you_ ?
2 Jodie, you haven't bought us presents, ... ?
3 Men hate shopping for clothes, ... ?
4 He didn't buy one of those amazing designer watches, ... ?
5 You know how to eat with chopsticks, ... ?
6 Well, that's what friends are for, ... ?

B 🔊 6.2 Listen and check.

Language note intonation

The intonation on question tags can rise or fall. Rising intonation means the question tag is a genuine question and the speaker is not sure what the answer will be. Falling intonation means the speaker is simply asking for agreement:

*You don't know where my keys are, **do you**?* (a real question – I don't know where my keys are.)

*It's a beautiful day, **isn't it**?* (not a real question – I'm expecting you to agree with me.)

C Listen again and mark the intonation of the question tags:
⟶ or ⟶ .

DEVELOPING WRITING
Using the right tone – complaining

A Read texts 1 and 2. Which one is for an Internet company to read and which is for other shoppers?

B Complete text 2 with the words in the box.

charge	warehouse	regular	grateful	courier
unacceptable	delay	quality	placed	helpdesk
resolve	make			

C Write an email (120–150 words) to an Internet company to ask for a refund. Choose from these problems:
- a mobile phone which was damaged when it arrived
- three CDs but only one was delivered
- a pair of trainers but the wrong size and colour were sent.

1

A load of rubbish ★ ☆ ☆ ☆ ☆

shopaholic   *Posted: 24/10*

Saw the jacket on the website and thought 'must have that'. It looked gorgeous on the model. Ordered the size and colour I wanted, paid extra for express delivery to arrive next day. Big mistake. It took ages and when I got it I couldn't believe my eyes. They'd sent wrong colour, leather was horrible – hard and cheap-looking – and jacket had tacky plastic buttons. That wasn't all. There was a big rip at the back, so I rang Customer Services. After hanging on phone for 45 mins, I got through and some woman said I must have damaged jacket and refused to give me my money back. What a joke!! Take a tip from me – never order from these idiots!!!

💬 Comments (7) | Was this review helpful? **yes** **no**

2

To
Subject   **Order number: 12897BLU**

I [1] .... an order for a leather jacket in dark blue from your website on 17/10. I paid an additional delivery [2] .... of £9.99 in order to receive the jacket the following day. The order failed to arrive and after a further [3] .... of six days, it was finally delivered. I am sorry to say it was not at all what I had expected. Not only had the [4] .... sent out the wrong colour, but the jacket was very disappointing. The leather was of very poor [5] .... and there was a large rip at the back. I tried to contact your customer [6] .... and when I eventually got through, the operator was extremely unhelpful. She accused me of damaging the jacket myself and refused to give me a refund. Despite repeated attempts to [7] .... the issue through customer services I now have to [8] .... a formal complaint. I have been a [9] .... customer of yours and I find the recent poor service [10] .... I would be [11] .... if you could refund the sum of £149.99 to my account and arrange for a [12] .... to collect the damaged jacket.

VOCABULARY Clothes and accessories

A Give possible answers for each category.

1 three things you can wear in winter
2 three things you wear for sport
3 three accessories worn by both men and women
4 three types of clothes and shoes usually worn only by women
5 three things you wear on your feet
6 three types of jewellery

B Choose the correct words.

1 A: What do you think of my outfit for Jo's wedding?
  B: Er, it's a bit ¹*bright / stripy*, with all those red and yellow flowers. Haven't you got anything else?
  A: But I like ²*colourful / plain* clothes. They go with my personality.
  B: Yes, but the bride is supposed to be the centre of attention, not you. How about a ³*scruffy / smart* suit in a ⁴*checked / nice* colour like pale blue?
  A: Sounds a bit old-fashioned. I want to look ⁵*trendy / tacky*, and anyway – like one of those ⁶*bland cool* supermodels you see in the magazines.

2 A: You look nice. That top really ⁷*matches / suits* you.
  B: Thanks. I shopped around for ages to find a top to ⁸*suit / match* this skirt and in the end I bought this one second-hand.
  A: Good for you. It's not worth paying for designer brands. I've just bought these trousers in the sales myself. The thing is they don't ⁹*fit / suit* me properly. They're a bit ¹⁰*little / tight*.
  A: Why didn't you try them on in the shop?
  B: Well, there was this huge queue for the changing rooms and they were a real bargain, so I just bought them. I thought they would ¹¹*match / go* with all my tops for work.

READING

A Read the article quickly. Then choose the best title.

a How supermarkets improve a local area
b How supermarkets get you to spend
c How supermarkets have changed

B Where would you find these things in a supermarket, according to the information in the article? Read the text again and match the things to the numbered areas of the plan.

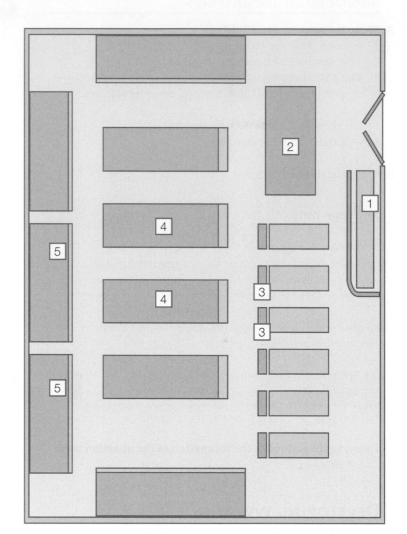

ice cream	......	bread	......
milk	......	a magazine	......
potatoes	......	trolleys and baskets	......
a tin of tomatoes	......	chewing gum	......
roses	......	strawberries	......

C Tick (✓) the true statements according to the article.

1 Buying healthy food at the start of a shopping trip makes shoppers feel good about themselves. ☑
2 Music can help persuade people to buy certain products. ☐
3 Colours in supermarkets are carefully chosen. ☐
4 The more products you see in a supermarket, the more you are likely to buy. ☐
5 Everyday items are easy to find in most supermarkets. ☐
6 Supermarkets like shoppers to finish their shopping as quickly as possible. ☐
7 Companies sometimes spend more money to have their products clearly displayed in a supermarket. ☐
8 The most expensive brands are often placed on the top shelf of a display. ☐

There are supermarkets in cities from Buenos Aires to Birmingham, so what is the secret of their success?

It all starts at the doors to the store. This is the usual position for trolleys and baskets. If you take a basket, you can carry more than in your hands. And taking a trolley is even better. The body of the trolley is much bigger than the average product, giving plenty of room to add more as you walk round the aisles. Flowers, fruit and vegetables are also often at the entrance. Flowers create a welcoming atmosphere, and buying fruit and vegetables makes you feel healthy. After you have chosen your apples, carrots and salad, you won't feel so guilty about picking up chocolate, crisps and beer later.

It's all about the senses. The smell of freshly-baked bread from a supermarket bakery makes you feel hungry, and so makes you buy more. Over two weeks, one supermarket played French or German music. When the French music was played, they sold more French wine and when they played German music, sales of German wine went up. Colour also has an effect. You will never see blue around food in a supermarket because it doesn't look good. Orange, red and pink aren't common either because they are colours that encourage you to move on.

The more you see, the more you shop. Fresh meat, fish and dairy products tend to be placed around the walls and outer parts of the store, whereas canned, frozen and processed foods are located towards the middle. This means you walk along nearly all the aisles to find everything you need. Essentials such as milk, bottled water or bread are often positioned at the back of the store, making you walk past hundreds of other products. Supermarkets are designed to make you stop as often as possible because of narrow aisles, special offers, or free samples.

SPECIAL OFFER

Every product has its place. New or popular items are often found at the end of aisles, on displays known as 'end caps'. Manufacturers pay extra for these prominent positions. Shelving is also important. The most expensive items are at adult eye level, with the brands above and below often at lower prices. Grabbing the first pack you see is easy, but might be hard on your pocket. And you don't escape when you queue up at the checkout. This is where you get bored waiting, and add magazines, sweets and chocolates to your trolley.

Glossary

trolley: a large container on wheels that you use for carrying things
aisles: /aɪlz/ passages between the shelves in a supermarket
dairy products: milk, and products made from milk
processed foods: food which has been dried or treated in some way

---

D Complete the conversation with the correct form of words from the article.

A: You were a long time at the supermarket.
B: Yes, sorry. They had lots of ¹ f..................... s..................... : cheese, biscuits, chocolate – so I tried some of each. Then I noticed all the ² s..................... o..................... around the store. You know - buy one, get one free, so I put my basket back and went for a ³ t..................... . I walked round all the ⁴ a..................... and ⁵ p..................... u..................... loads of bargains. The store was really busy, so I had to ⁶ q..................... u..................... for ages to pay at the ⁷ c..................... .
A: Right. So, where is all the shopping?
B: Oh, I couldn't carry it, so they're going to deliver it later today. If you spend over £75, you get free delivery.
A: But to be honest, it isn't really free. It cost us £75.

GRAMMAR *Must*

A Make guesses with *must* and the phrases in the box.

train for hours	love shopping	take her ages
be stuck	have a sale	be fed up
be going	be freezing	

1 A: Naomi looks nice in that outfit.
   B: Yes, she .... to a party.
2 A: Why don't you put on a thick jumper? You
   .... in that T-shirt.
   B: No, I'm OK, actually.
3 A: Lisa from HR and Mike from Sales haven't arrived
   yet.
   B: They .... in traffic. There are roadworks on
   the motorway.
4 A: Look at the queues outside that clothes shop.
   B: I guess they .... this week.
5 A: Every time I see Jack he's got a new mobile or some
   new clothes.
   B: You're right there. He ....
6 A: Sharon is so fit.
   B: I know. She .... every day at the gym.
7 A: I bought a pair of designer shoes but they only
   lasted a month before they fell apart.
   B: You .... about that.
8 A: Melanie always looks so smart. She wears outfits
   with matching accessories and her hair and make-
   up are always perfect.
   B: It .... to get ready to go out.

B Write the words in the correct order.

1 mall / the / check / you / must / really / out / new /
   shopping
   ....
2 your / market / to / must / you / simply / souvenirs /
   go / the / for
   ....
3 in / when / local / try / you / must / the / wine / you're
   / Valencia
   ....
4 holiday / you're / old / must / you / visit / the / town /
   while / on / here
   ....
5 for / the / restaurant / to / must / you / really / go /
   fish / dinner
   ....

C Complete the sentences with *must, mustn't, had to,* or *will have to.*

1 I .... forget to top-up my mobile later. I'm really low
   on credit.
2 Yesterday was a nightmare. I .... work until 9 p.m. to
   meet a deadline.
3 We'll lend you the money, but you .... pay us back in
   a couple of weeks.
4 I'm not supposed to tell anyone about my new job so I
   .... say any more.
5 When I was a child, I .... do as I was told.
6 I've just got my credit card bill. I .... make sure I pay it
   this week.
7 Kelly is leaving the company soon. We .... remember
   to get her a card and present.
8 In the future, people .... save energy and use their
   cars less.

D Nancy is a very bossy person at home and at work. Tick the
appropriate sentence (a or b) to make her sound more polite.

At work

1 'You mustn't send personal emails from your computer.'
   a You're not allowed to send personal emails from your
     computer. ✓
   b If I were you, I wouldn't send personal emails from your
     computer. ☐
2 'You must go on that training course.'
   a If I were you, I would go on that training course. ☐
   b You're allowed to go on that training course. ☐
3 'You mustn't take more than an hour for lunch.'
   a You don't have to take more than an hour for lunch. ☐
   b You aren't supposed to take more than an hour for lunch. ☐

At home

4 'You must feed the dog every morning.'
   a Please feed the dog every morning. ☐
   b You can feed the dog every morning. ☐
5 'You mustn't stay out later than midnight.'
   a If I were you, I wouldn't stay out later than midnight. ☐
   b You're not allowed to stay out later than midnight. ☐
6 'You must open a bank account for your savings.'
   a You're supposed to open a bank account for your savings. ☐
   b If I were you, I'd open a bank account for your savings. ☐

Language note *mustn't / don't have to*

- -

Don't confuse the negative forms *mustn't* and
don't have to.
I **mustn't buy** any more clothes.
(= It's important for me not to spend any more money.)
I **don't have to buy** any more clothes.
(= It isn't necessary. I have enough already.)

DEVELOPING CONVERSATIONS
Responding to recommendations

Write the lines of the correct conversation in the gaps below.

> I'm thinking of buying some souvenirs before we head home.
> Well, you could try the old town. There are lots of gift shops there.
> No, he doesn't want to do that. You can pre-book at the cinema now. I'd go online and check out their website.
> I'd like to get some tickets for the new James Bond film next week.
> No, you don't want to go there. It's a rip-off. You'd be better going to the market. They have lots of nice hand-made stuff there.
> Well, go early to queue and get tickets. Lots of people want to see it.

Conversation 1

A: *I'm thinking of buying some souvenirs before we head home.*

B: ....

....

C: ....

....

Conversation 2

A: ....

....

B: ....

....

C: ....

....

Vocabulary Builder Quiz 6 (*OVB* pp22–24)

Try the *OVB* quiz for Unit 6. Write your answers in your notebook. Then check them and record your score.

A Find the error in the sentences below and correct it.
1 Here's the €20 I own you.
2 I don't like bright colours. My clothes are pretty plait.
3 Which bland of coffee do you usually buy?
4 We bought a beautiful curved wooden box in Bali.
5 Have you been to the new shopping hall yet?
6 She got married in a lovely sink dress.
7 Apparently, there are a lot of cake £20 notes going around.
8 It's boiling. Why are you wearing such a think jumper?

B Match the sentence halves.
1 Hello. Come in. Shall I   a out of business.
2 Lots of smaller shops have gone   b without buying something every week.
3 I'm a shopaholic. I can't go   c around outside the newsagent's?
4 My finances are a mess. I've just gone   d overdrawn by about £500.
5 I need to lose some weight. It's time to   e hang up your coat?
6 Why are those kids hanging   f go on a diet.

C Complete the sentences with an expression based on *out*.
1 The defender has been badly injured so he's ....
2 Hardly anyone wears suits to work nowadays. They're ....
3 The gang has been arrested and so the public is now ....
4 We had to throw away lots of the food in the freezer. It was all ....
5 He swore at the teacher and was thrown ....
6 Joe has had his operation and he should be ....next week.

D Which word do you need to complete the sentences in each set?
1 I took the jeans back because they didn't .... me. Mum's old furniture won't .... in her new flat. 50 guests in our tiny flat will be a tight ....
2 It's the wrong colour blue – it doesn't .... your top. We're hoping to .... last year's sales. If the blood types don't ...., they can't arrest him.
3 We had to .... up for hours to get tickets. It really annoys me when people jump the .... We got to the front of the .... after about an hour.
4 She won't buy anything without a designer .... I washed my silk top without checking the .... Don't forget to .... your luggage.
5 Most clothes nowadays are .... produced. There was a .... protest against the taxes. We're entering a period of .... unemployment.

Score ___/25

**Wait a couple of weeks and try the quiz again.
Compare your scores.**

VOCABULARY Describing courses

A What sort of course should these people go on? Match the statements (1–6) to the courses (a–f).

1 I'm taking a group of teenagers on an adventure holiday and I'm a bit worried in case one of them has an accident. It's important for me to know what to do. ......

2 I'm at home with a young family all day, so the only time I can study is when they're in bed. I want to do a computer course and I'd like to have the opportunity to meet some new people. ......

3 All my friends are in their 60s and they're getting into emailing and the Internet. I'm hopeless with technology but it's about time I caught up. ......

4 I travel for my job, so I'm never available at the same times every week. I'm good with computers but I'd like to learn new skills. ......

5 I really enjoyed my first degree and I've done quite well in my career. But I'd like to get back to university now and do a master's or something like that. ......

6 I love my job but I'm really bad at giving presentations. It's a bit worrying because I'm presenting at a big conference soon. ......

a a postgraduate course
b a first-aid course
c an evening course
d an online course
e an IT course
f a training course in public speaking

B Choose a word for describing courses, to complete all the sentences in each set (1–8).

1 Have you chosen which ..... *modules* ..... you want to do?
French language, literature and History are core ..... *modules* ..... in my first year.
Spanish and French are optional ..... *modules* ..... on my course.
Last year was fine but the ..... *modules* ..... this year are much harder.

2 The .... for your essays is Friday the 19th.
A week to do all that reading – it's a very tight ....
I was ill for a couple of weeks and I missed the ....
I'm behind so I'm going to ask Mr Clarke if I can extend the ....

3 Excuse me, where's .... theatre 2?
Can you believe it? I fell asleep in the history ....
That was a fascinating .... Dr King really brought the subject to life.
I don't think I could ever give a .... – I'd be much too nervous.

4 I've just met my personal .... – she seems really nice.
I'm really lucky to have a dedicated and supportive ....
I'm not getting on very well because I don't have a very helpful ....

5 Once I've finished my final .... I'll start looking for a job. Congratulations! Misha was telling me you passed all your .... Do you have to repeat the course if you fail your .... ? I can't wait for the summer, but I have to get through the end-of-year .... first.

6 I have a weekly .... with about seven or eight other students.
I think I get more out of .... discussions than studying on my own.
Sorry, I can't stay for a chat. I have to go to a ....
Henry likes the sound of his own voice. He always talks too much when we have a group ....

7 I'm writing an .... just now, so I can't come to the cinema.
When do we have to hand in our .... ?
I have to do a 2 000-word .... by Monday. I'll never make it.

8 How are things? Are you coping with the .... ?
I think I might change course. Medicine has such a heavy ....
We'd better start studying at bit harder. They increase the .... in the second year.
You're so lucky studying IT – you have a much lighter .... than me.

C Look at the tips for getting the most out of a course. Which nouns from exercise B are the people talking about?

1 Take your time when making your choices. If you sign up for the wrong subjects, you can waste quite a lot of time. ..... *modules* .....

2 Give them respect but remember they are there to help you. If you have a problem or question, don't be afraid to say so. ....

3 Plan your time so that you can divide up the work before the key date. Don't leave everything to the last minute, but you can ask for more time if you have been ill. ....

4 Make a contribution to each one but don't take the session over. Let other students speak. ....

5 Learn to take notes efficiently. If the speaker isn't very interesting, give him or her some feedback on how they come across. ....

6 All the content must be your own work, so don't copy sections of text from the Internet. Staff will recognise this and you will get caught out. ....

DEVELOPING CONVERSATIONS

How's the course going?

> **Language note** school vs university
>
> At school, students have **teachers** and **lessons**, at university they have **tutors** / **lecturers** and **lectures**. You can use the word **student** for someone who is at university / college, but a child at school is usually called a **pupil**.

Choose the correct words.

1 A: How's the IT course going?
  B: To be honest, I'm finding it really *hard / hardly*. I'm *failing / struggling* with the workload just now. I can't keep up.

2 A: How are the lessons going?
  B: Quite *fine / well*, actually. I'm *doing / making* good progress.

3 A: How's the training course going?
  B: *Really / Real* well. I'm enjoying *me / it*.

4 A: How's the course going?
  B: Well, I've *been / had* a few ups and downs, but the modules are getting easier this *seminar / term*.

5 A: How's it going at school?
  B: OK, but we're doing our *final / last* exams at the moment, so I have to do loads of *revision / essays*.

6 A: How are the exams going?
  B: Oh, I've just finished them, actually. But I've still got a 10 000-word essay to *bring / hand* in. If I *fail / miss* the deadline, I won't get my degree.

GRAMMAR *After, once and when*

A Tick (✓) the correct sentences. Correct the incorrect ones.

1 I should have more time once the course finishes next week. ☐

2 What are you planning to do after your evening course finished? ☐

3 Once I will meet the other students on the course, I'll feel less nervous. ☐

4 I hope to extend the essay deadline once I spoke to my tutor. ☐

5 Why don't we go away for the weekend after we get our exam results? ☐

6 When the tutor's arrived, we'll start the seminar. ☐

7 We're going to have a huge party when the final exams will be over. ☐

8 After I left college, I'll get a part-time job. ☐

B Complete the sentences with the correct form of the verbs in the box.

hand / catch	apologise / see
let / receive	be / finish
come / do	feel / get

1 A: How's the course going?
  B: To be honest, I'*ll be*............. glad when it*'s finished*...... . I'm exhausted!

2 A: How did you do in your exams?
  B: I haven't had the results yet. I .... you know when I .... them.

3 A: How come you're staying in tonight?
  B: I have to finish an essay. I .... out with you after I .... it.

4 A: What's the student accommodation like?
  B: Not great, but I've only been there a week. I .... better once I .... used to it.

5 A: You look a bit tired.
  B: I'm struggling with my workload at the moment. Once I .... in my essay, I .... up on my sleep.

6 A: I can't believe you fell asleep in the lecture!
  B: Don't remind me. I .... to Dr Richter when I .... him.

VOCABULARY Forming words

A Complete the list with the correct form of the words in brackets. Use a dictionary to help you.

> **Life skills**
>
> The term 'life skills' is sometimes used to refer to basic skills people need to survive in the adult world. Here is a possible list:
>
> a ......*social*...... (society) skills ☐
> b money .... (manage) skills ☐
> c .... (know) of a foreign language ☐
> d basic .... (cook) skills ☐
> e taking care of your personal
> .... (appear) ☐
> f the .... (able) to drive ☐
> g .... (communicate) skills ☐
> h an .... (understand) of local
> politics ☐
> i dealing with personal ....
> (relation) ☐

B Number the list in B in the order of importance for young people in your country.

C Complete the words with the endings in the box.

-ation (x2)	-ment	-ments	-ure	-al (x2)
-ity	-ations			

Great expectations

What is ¹ ...*education*... for? To give young people ² inform...................... about different subjects or to prepare them for the adult world? If it's the second of these, then I'm a complete ³ fail...................... I left university with a first-class degree but no ⁴ practic...................... skills at all. Even today, my wife is the one with life skills. She works out the ⁵ calcul...................... of the interest on our loans, knows the best ⁶ treat...................... for cuts and bruises, and can explain local ⁷ elect...................... to our son. If the computer goes wrong, she's got the ⁸ technic...................... knowledge to put it right. She also has the ⁹ abil...................... to sort out ¹⁰ argu...................... between my sister and me. Oh, and she's also a very talented writer. I enjoyed my degree but maybe I should have taken a first-aid course and a cookery course as well.

LISTENING

A 🔊 **7.1 You are going to hear interviews with people in the street about what makes a good school. Listen and number the topics in the order you hear them.**

home education ......
the role of teachers ......
discipline ......
'whole child' education ......
the role of parents ......
boarding school ......

B 🔊 **7.1 Listen again. Tick (✓) the opinions / statements that are given in the interviews?**

1 Independent schools are better than state schools. ☐
2 Teachers in Britain should be more strict. ☐
3 It's the teacher's job to encourage students. ☐
4 Home education is becoming more and more popular. ☐
5 Home education gives students more control over
their learning. ☐
6 The Montessori approach doesn't teach children in groups. ☐
7 Teachers don't need to have a positive attitude to
their students. ☐
8 Parents are important in making a good school. ☐

PRONUNCIATION word stress

A Mark the main stress in the underlined words.
1 Good teachers can be an <u>inspiration</u> to their class and <u>encourage</u> them to do well.
2 Sir, would you mind if I asked you a question about <u>education</u>?
3 Maria Montessori was an Italian woman who developed an approach to <u>educate</u> the whole child.
4 Of course, the teacher can give <u>encouragement</u> and try to <u>inspire</u> the class, but if a child won't <u>co-operate</u>, then there's little we can do.
5 So, it's all about <u>co-operation</u> between teachers and families.

B 🔊 **7.2 Listen and check.**

> **Learner tip**
>
> Getting word stress right is important in overall fluency. Although there are no simple rules relating to word stress, there are some common patterns, e.g. when adding *-tion* to form a noun, and *-ese* to form an adjective:
>
> <u>o</u>rganise organi<u>sa</u>tion
> comm<u>u</u>nicate communi<u>ca</u>tion
>
> <u>Ja</u>pan Japan<u>ese</u>
> <u>Por</u>tugal Portug<u>uese</u>

READING

A **Read the article quickly. What is the main reason for writing it?**
a to promote online learning
b to introduce readers to a new way of learning
c to give a profile of a talented student

B **Are these statements true or false?**
1 Martina doesn't have a regular work timetable.
2 She is doing an online course to improve her professional skills.
3 Online learning lets her work as slowly or quickly as she likes.
4 She wishes her tutor was more supportive.
5 She says that online courses are similar to traditional learning in some ways.
6 Online learners never see each other face to face.
7 Martina is taking a postgraduate course.

C **Choose the correct prepositions. Look back at the article if you need to.**
1 We've spent a long time on that topic, so it's time to move *on / off.*
2 Take an active part *in / of* the seminars if you want to get the most out of the course.
3 There are no exams on my drama course. It's great to do something just *with / for* the love of it.
4 I've no idea why I went *to / for* the philosophy module – it's way over my head!
5 Home education means students can work *to / in* their own time and *at / with* their own pace.
6 I've kept *in / to* touch with all my friends from university.

LEARNING FOR LIFE

More and more people are turning to online learning to improve their skills or to study a subject just for the love of it. We talked to Martina Connor, a keen online student, to find out what it's all about.

Q What made you choose online learning?

A Well, it suits me because of my job. I work shifts, so I'm never available at the same time each week. The local college offers some interesting evening courses, but they run at the same time as one of my shifts. With online learning, I can work in my own time and fit my studies around work and my social life.

Q How did you get started?

A I hadn't planned to go back to studying, but then I came across a TV programme on the history of art and I found the whole thing fascinating. I did a search on the Internet and I found an organisation that offered good courses, but also the flexibility I need. I have to work at my own pace because of my job. So, I registered, downloaded the course materials and I've been studying ever since.

Q But don't you need a teacher?

A To be honest, thanks to the Internet, I can get the same support as students in a more traditional classroom. I have a personal tutor – she's very experienced in working with online students. We keep in touch by phone or email. I can download her lectures and study notes. She gives me regular assignments and marks my work, just like doing homework from school, really.

Q What about testing?

A There's no way of skipping tests just because I study at home! When I've done a section of a module, I complete a series of worksheets online to check that I've got the main points. I also have to do written assignments, which are marked by my tutor. Then at the end of each core module, there's a long essay to write. You can't move on to the next module unless you get a good mark.

Q Don't you miss contact with other students?

A In fact, there's a big community of online learners. Interactive technology means we can take part in virtual lessons and seminars. We also have the students' forum. That's where you can chat online, and exchange ideas and advice. It's great for your social life, too. Students in the same area often get together for a coffee or a beer.

Q What do you have in mind for after the course?

A I'm not sure. I have four more modules to do but when I've finished, I might go for the degree course or choose something different.

Glossary

register: to put your personal details and other information on an official list
virtual: appearing on computers or in the Internet

VOCABULARY
Schools, teachers and students

A Complete the conversation with the phrases in the box.

had a good reputation	hardly any facilities
skipping classes	a very good head teacher
a bright girl and she's very studious	Discipline wasn't very good

A: Why did Kiera change schools in the middle of a term?

B: Well, she moved because she wasn't happy at Highlands School. There were ¹ ....

A: I thought it ² .... for sport.

B: Yes, but not enough computers, no music room or after-school clubs.

A: Oh, I didn't realise.

B: And she said it was quite rough. ³ .... there and there were problems with bullying.

A: That's surprising. My neighbour was telling me it had ⁴ .... Poor Kiera, though. She's such ⁵ ....

B: Actually, she was really unhappy there and she refused to go. She was in serious trouble because she kept ⁶ .... But she's much happier now.

A: I'm glad everything is OK.

B Find and correct eight mistakes in the conversation.

A: What's your new French teacher like?

B: Much better than our old teacher. She was quite ~~tradition~~ *traditional*. I really enjoy Mr Holland's lessons. He's lively and he does things fun. But he's good at control the class, too. You know Sharon Dodd, the one who never gives attention in class?

A: Oh, I know her – she thinks she knows all it.

B: Yeah, right, well, she was messing about and he sent her to the head teacher straightaway.

A: Good for him.

B: So what's your new football coach like?

A: He's good. He really push us in the training sessions and he's very encouragement when we play well. But he's quite patience if we make mistakes.

B: Sounds great.

GRAMMAR
Zero conditionals and first conditionals

A Match the sentence halves to make zero conditionals.

1 If you don't clean a cut,
2 When you click on 'New',
3 If you are late three times in the same week,
4 When you mix blue and yellow,
5 When Annie drinks cola,
6 If you don't attend 90 per cent of the lectures,

a you can't continue the module.
b you get a detention.
c it opens a document.
d she gets a headache.
e you get green.
f it gets infected.

B Complete the first conditional sentences with the pairs of verbs in the box. Make any necessary changes to the verbs.

take / get	might get / download
~~start / meet~~	misbehave / send
get / not pass	might call / have
continue / be suspended	fancy / be

1 If you ....*start*.... the essay now, you.*'ll meet*......... the deadline easily.

2 I .... my tutor if I .... problems with this assignment – it's quite difficult.

3 If you .... less that 50 per cent in the exam, you ....

4 .... a break if you .... fed up with your revision.

5 If James .... to bully other students, he .... from school.

6 You .... caught if you .... your answers from the Internet.

7 If you .... talking the essay through, I .... in my office until seven this evening.

8 If Amy .... in class again, I .... her to the head teacher.

DEVELOPING WRITING
A course review – giving feedback

A Read student feedback from two different courses. Which course was more successful?

B Choose the correct words in text A opposite.

A

I ¹ *completely / thoroughly* enjoyed the course. Overall, it was a positive learning ² *experience / experiment*, which fully met my expectations. The training was of a high ³ *standard / level*. The course was well ⁴ *run / made*, with a good selection of topics and plenty of opportunities to learn from other students. The sessions were challenging but the hands-on practice made them very ⁵ *rewarded / rewarding*. Completing a short ⁶ *worksheet / homework* after each session helped me check progress and review key points. The clear and helpful handouts summarised the main points of each session. The tutors all had excellent knowledge of their subject but were able to communicate clearly with students of different levels. They were also easy to talk to and willing to give individual ⁷ *supportive / support* where necessary. The training centre had good ⁸ *technology / facilities* and all the equipment worked well. I have a genuine sense of ⁹ *achievement / achieving* after completing the course and I would definitely ¹⁰ *propose / recommend* it to others.

B

I'm afraid that the course didn't live up to my expectations. Overall, I thought the training was quite poor. I was hoping for some practical sessions, but the three days consisted of long lectures with no group work. The content of the first day was inappropriate for postgraduate students – it was more undergraduate level. The tutors didn't seem very well prepared. There were no handouts provided after any of the lectures, forcing us to take long sets of notes each day. The lecture theatres were well-equipped but the tutors didn't appear to know how to use the interactive whiteboard, or even the microphone. We were given a very tight deadline for the end-of-course essay and I struggled to get it finished. I'm sorry to say that the course wasn't a very good use of my time. I don't really feel I achieved any of my goals or even that I learnt anything new. Perhaps you could review the course content and choice of tutors for future courses.

C Look at the feedback in text B again. **Underline the more polite ways of saying these things.**
1 I wasted three days.
2 The training was hopeless.
3 You got the level wrong.
4 The tutors must be technophobes.
5 You gave us too much work.
6 Get it right next time.

D Write feedback (120–150 words) for a course (real or imaginary). Include your general opinion and comments on some of the following aspects of the course.
- level
- pace
- tuition / training
- materials and handouts
- facilities
- workload

Vocabulary Builder Quiz 7 (*OVB* pp26–28)

Try the *OVB* quiz for Unit 7. Write your answers in your notebook. Then check them and record your score.

A Complete the sentences with nouns that end in *-tion* and *-ment*.
1 I think continuous ....ment of students is much fairer than just exams.
2 Nursing is a job where you need patience and ....tion.
3 It was hard to concentrate during the meeting because there were a lot of ....tions.
4 Climbing Mount Everest is such an incredible ....ment. You must be very proud.
5 They're doing some tests and keeping him in hospital for a few days for ....tion.
6 My tutor always gives us lots of ....ment, so we feel that we're making progress.

B Tick (✓) the six adjectives that form their opposite with *in-*.
- ☐ relevant
- ☐ intelligent
- ☐ experienced
- ☐ convenient
- ☐ complete
- ☐ sensitive
- ☐ practical
- ☐ accurate
- ☐ decisive
- ☐ fit

C Complete the conversations with words from boxes A and B for each sentence.

A get hand in pay go through extend do

| B some revision the deadline the notes attention |
| a detention my assignment |

1 A: I'm just going to .... to the tutor. I'm glad I've finished it.
   B: Oh, no. I forgot all about that. Do you think Mrs Grange will .... by a few days?
2 A: Oh, no. We've got a chemistry test next week. I need to .... this weekend.
   B: Why don't we .... from this term together? We can help each other.
   A: How's school?
   B: Not great. The teacher says I need to stop talking in class and .... to the lesson. If I get caught again, I'll ....

D Read the statements. Is each opinion positive (✓) or negative (✗)?
1 The parents of the kids at that school are really pushy. ☐
2 The whole course was a complete failure. ☐
3 The students all deserved to do well. ☐
4 They have very impressive facilities at the new college. ☐
5 I owe my teacher a huge debt of gratitude. ☐
6 It's so unfair. She was such a cheat. ☐
7 The school didn't live up to its good reputation. ☐

Score ____/25

Wait a couple of weeks and try the quiz again. Compare your scores.

08 EATING

VOCABULARY Describing food

A Complete the dialogues with the pairs of verbs in the box.

roast / grill	mash / grate	steam / boil
deep-fry / stir-fry	slice / marinate	

1 A: If you .... vegetables, rather than
      .... them, you keep in more of the vitamins.
    B: Oh, I didn't know that.
2 A: Please don't .... the fish in all that oil. Why
      don't you .... it, the Chinese way?
    B: I've never tried cooking that way.
3 A: Can I give you a hand?
    B: Yes, please. If you could .... the potatoes
      and .... the cheese, that would be a help.
4 A: That knife's very sharp – be careful when you
      .... the meat.
    B: OK. How long does it need to .... in the
      wine for?
5 A: How are you going to cook the chicken pieces?
    B: It's a waste of electricity to .... them in the
      oven, so I think I'll .... them.

B Cross out the foods that do not go with the ways of cooking.

1 grill   fish / cake / chicken / steak
2 slice   tomatoes / cheese / cake / sauce
3 mash   bread / potatoes / bananas / baby food
4 steam   couscous / vegetables / fish / soup
5 deep-fry   chips / trifle / fish / squid
6 roast   eggs / beef / chicken / duck
7 boil   pasta / potatoes / salad / rice
8 grate   carrots / oysters / cheese / apples
9 marinate   prawns / meat / chicken / rice
10 stir-fry   vegetables / meat / fruit / seafood

C Complete the adjectives for describing food.

1 She makes wonderful desserts but everything comes
   with cream and chocolate. It's just so f _ _ _ _ _ _ _ _ .
2 Since Lindsay came back from Mexico, everything comes
   with chillies. It's much too s _ _ _ _ for me.
3 That sauce was really t _ _ _ _ _ – what herbs did you add
   to it?
4 I admit I'm a bit fussy. I'm not keen on fish and I never
   eat fried food. It's just too g _ _ _ _ _ _ .
5 My pasta is a bit b _ _ _ _ . Could you pass the salt?
6 The steak and chips were really f _ _ _ _ _ _ _ . I don't
   think I can eat any more.

D Which is the odd one out?

1	corn on the cob	limes	spinach	radishes
2	tripe	squid	shrimps	oysters
3	kebabs	squid	trifle	olives
4	ice cream	trifle	cake	peanuts
5	blue cheese	steak	kebabs	chicken

DEVELOPING CONVERSATIONS
Describing dishes

Write answers for the questions. Write the words in brackets in the correct order.

1 A: What's a 'lime'?
    B: .... (fruit / it's / of / kind / a).
      .... (a / but / it's / a / like / bit / lemon)
      smaller and green.
2 A: What's 'black pepper'?
    B: .... (of / kind / a / spice / it's) like
      Cayenne pepper .... (but / as / it's /
      not / strong)
3 A: What's 'strawberry fool'?
    B: .... (a / it's / kind / of) dessert.
      .... (mashed / from / made / it's) fruit
      and cream.
4 A: What's 'tofu'?
    B: .... (like / it's / a / bit / cheese / but)
      more bland. .... (from / soya / beans /
      made / it's / mashed) and it's used in Asian cookery.
5 A: What's 'wiejska'?
    B: .... (from / of / sausage / a / kind /
      it's) Poland. .... (pork / from / made /
      it's), and different herbs and spices.

READING

A **Look at the headings in the article. Where might this type of text appear?**
a   on a website on how to cook
b   in a magazine on food and nutrition
c   in a dieter's blog

B **Read the article, which describes four different eating patterns. Match the questions (1–10) to the correct text (A–D).**
Which person:
1   tends not to eat breakfast? ☐☐
2   doesn't really enjoy eating? ☐☐☐
3   eats regular meals? ☐
4   doesn't concentrate just on eating? ☐
5   avoids bland food? ☐
6   doesn't get what their body needs from their diet? ☐☐☐
7   eats small amounts throughout the day? ☐
8   often eats alone? ☐
9   tend to eat too much? ☐
10   eats quickly? ☐☐

C **Replace the underlined words in the sentences with the words and phrases in the box.**

from scratch	counts	bite to eat
proper	appetite	missed out on
a lack of	go all day without food	

1   Shall we have a <u>snack</u> before we start the decorating? ....
2   It's such a shame. He <u>lost the opportunity of</u> opening his own restaurant. ....
3   I never buy ready meals. I think it's fun to prepare food <u>from the beginning</u>. ....
4   It can't be good for you to <u>not eat until the evening</u>. ....
5   I'm starving when I get up in the morning. I never leave the house without a <u>good</u> breakfast. ....
6   For me, it's health that <u>is important</u> – that's why I buy organic food. ....
7   No wonder she's so slim, she has a very small <u>desire for food</u>. ....
8   <u>Not having</u> variety in your diet can create health problems. ....

What kind of eater are you?

A **The fruit-free zone** This is someone who eats a fairly unadventurous diet of mainly protein and carbohydrates. A typical meal might consist of just meat and potatoes, or steak and chips. Any vegetables they eat tend to be frozen and easy to prepare, such as peas or sweetcorn. They hardly ever eat fresh fruit – occasionally an orange or an apple, or some fruit juice. Although they eat three meals a day, they take little pleasure in eating and have little variety in their diet. The lack of fruit and vegetables means they are probably missing out on vitamins, minerals and other nutrients.

B **The general grazer** This person doesn't often sit down to a proper meal, preferring to just grab smaller bites to eat throughout the day. Not a fan of breakfast, by mid-morning they will start a series of 'mini-meals' – a sandwich, then 15 minutes later some fruit, then half an hour later some biscuits, followed by various snacks throughout the day. Often eating quickly and while doing other activities – working, watching TV, even driving – they get little satisfaction from food. They have no control over their appetite and will often overeat on foods of little nutritional value.

C **The fast-food fan** For this person, it's convenience that counts. Often with a busy lifestyle, they tell themselves they don't have time to shop for fresh ingredients and cook them from scratch. Their food of choice is often tasty and filling, but can be greasy and fattening. A typical lunch might be hamburger and fries, followed in the evening by a ready meal or takeaway curry and rice. They tend to like strong flavours, and find fresh fruit and vegetables rather bland. High levels of fats, sugars and salts in their diet create potential health problems.

D **The evening eater** This is someone who often goes all day without eating anything at all. They will almost certainly skip breakfast and if you invite them for lunch, they will usually make an excuse about being too busy. By dinner time, they are starving hungry, and so consume a huge number of calories in one go. The evening meal itself may be followed by a range of sweet or salty snacks to fill the need for food that was missed during the day. Preferring to eat by themselves, they tend to be fast eaters who don't take part in shared meals with family or friends.

Glossary

protein: a substance in meat, eggs, etc. that helps people grow and be healthy
carbohydrates: a substance in bread, potatoes, etc. that provides the body with energy
minerals / nutrients: substances in food that people need for good health

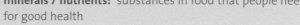

GRAMMAR *Tend to*

A Write these sentences in the negative. Give two different negative forms.

1 I tend to have a proper breakfast every morning.
I don't tend to / tend not to have a proper breakfast every morning.

2 We tend to split the bill when we eat out.
We ....

3 As kids, we tended to eat lots of sugary snacks.
As kids, ...

4 Since his illness, he's tended to pay attention to his diet.
Since his illness, ...

5 My mum tends to use a recipe book when she cooks.
My mum ....

6 As a student, she tended to eat tinned and frozen food.
As a student, ...

B Complete the sentences with the correct form of *tend to*.

1 A: My kids are just so fussy. They won't eat anything but meat and potatoes.
   B: Don't worry. Children .... grow out of that and become more adventurous

2 A: Ali was telling me you've become a vegetarian. Don't you miss a nice steak and chips?
   B: Well, I .... eat much meat anyway, so it's no problem.

3 A: We're visiting Italy later this year. Do you know how much people .... tip in restaurants?
   B: I think service is included in the bill.

4 A: You're always cooking lots of spinach and stuff like that.
   B: I know. Isn't it funny how tastes change? When I was a teenager I .... leave all my vegetables on the side of my plate. Now I love them.

5 A: I've got three vegetarians coming to dinner. What .... you .... cook that's tasty but meat-free?
   B: Why don't I lend you my veggie recipe book? It's got loads of great ideas.

6 A: Do you like spicy food?
   B: Well, up until now, I .... be quite an unadventurous eater, but I tried Thai curry recently and it was really tasty.

7 A: No wine for me, thanks. I .... drink during the week.
   B: Me neither.

8 A: It's very quiet in the restaurant tonight.
   B: Yes, there .... be a lot of customers on Mondays.

LISTENING

📻 **8.1 You are going to hear a presenter and chef on a TV cookery programme. Listen and complete the recipe.**

Cheesy pasta with spinach
Serves: 4

Ingredients

1 medium onion, peeled and chopped
a .... spinach, washed and finely chopped
b .... pasta
2 tbsp extra virgin olive oil
a little c ....
a handful of basil leaves
100g d .... cheese

Method

- Cook the pasta in a large pan of e .... salted water for about f .... minutes. Don't let it overcook.
- Heat the oil and butter in a frying pan over a g .... heat and add the onions. Fry gently for about five minutes until soft and golden.
- Turn the heat down, and add the h .... to the frying pan. Mix it gently with the onions until it cooks down (1–2 minutes). There's no need to boil or i .... it first.
- Drain the pasta really well. Add it to the onion and spinach, and mix well.
- Add in the cheese and the basil leaves and give one final stir.

Alternatives

- Add a few j .... and some garlic to the basic recipe.
- If you eat meat or fish, add some chicken or k .... to the onions and fry gently until cooked.

PRONUNCIATION Long vowel sounds

A 🔊 **8.2 Listen to these long vowel sounds.**

/iː/   /ɑː/   /uː/   /ɜː/   /ɔː/

B Match the symbols to the underlined words from *Listening*.

1 This is fast <u>food</u>, but home style.   /uː/
2 How many people will it <u>feed</u>?
3 This is a dish for <u>four</u> people.
4 <u>First</u> thing is to get the pasta cooking.
5 We need a <u>large</u> saucepan of boiling salted water.

C Which letters in bold have a different sound?

1 pra**w**n   **c**orn   p**o**rtion   f**o**reign
2 st**a**rving   over**cha**rged   m**a**rinate   h**a**lf
3 ch**ee**se   st**ea**m   r**i**ch   p**ea**nut
4 déc**o**r   t**u**rn   st**i**r   des**e**rted
5 tablesp**oo**n   s**ou**p   t**ou**gh   f**oo**d

D 🔊 **8.3 Listen and check.**

DEVELOPING WRITING

An encyclopedia entry – describing food culture

A Read the encyclopedia entry about Japanese food. Underline three more sentences that the editor would ask to be taken out because they express opinion rather than fact.

B Correct the mistakes in these phrases about food and eating. Look back at the text if you need to.

1 Pasta is a basic of the Italian diet.
2 The Polish eat a large varied of pork dishes.
3 Fish and seafood appear strongly in the coastal areas of Spain.
4 The best-knowed dishes in Argentina are *asado*s.
5 The food in Hong Kong consists with a huge range of ingredients.
6 Duck is popular in Singapore served with a range of side plates.
7 Lunch is the principal meal of the day in Brazil.
8 It's bad taste to start eating before the other people at the table.

C Write two paragraphs (120–150 words) for an online encyclopedia about the food culture in your country. Use some of the headings and the language in the text to help you.

> **Learner tip**
>
> When you write, remember to think who your reader is and why they are reading the text, e.g. in a factual piece of writing, they won't expect to find your personal opinions, or likes and dislikes.

Japanese cuisine

Basic ingredients

Rice is a staple of the Japanese diet and is served with nearly every meal. Noodles are also popular for light meals. The Japanese eat a huge variety of fish and seafood including tuna, squid, octopus and shellfish. Soy products also feature strongly in soy sauce, tofu and miso (a soya paste used in soups). <u>Miso soup is my personal favourite.</u>

Typical dishes

The best-known styles of Japanese food are sashimi (sliced raw fish) eaten with wasabi (a spicy green horseradish paste) and soy sauce. Sushi is raw fish and rice in seaweed, cut into small pieces and served with soy sauce and wasabi. You can buy sushi all over the world now but it won't be as good as in Japan. Tempura consists of vegetables or seafood coated in batter and deep-fried. Sukiyaki is a stew of beef, cooked together in sake (rice wine), sugar and soy sauce. It is served with vegetables, and tofu.

Daily eating

People in Japan generally eat three meals a day: breakfast, lunch and dinner. A traditional breakfast consists of steamed rice, miso soup, and side dishes like pickles, grilled fish and dried seaweed. Some families now eat a Western-style breakfast of cereal, toast, milk and fruit juice. Dinner is the main meal of the day and may be traditional Japanese-style or a dish from another cuisine such as Italian, Chinese, French or American. I'm really worried that our traditional cuisine may be changing because of imported food.

Table manners

It's important to say traditional phrases at the beginning and end of a meal: itadakimasu ('I gratefully receive') and gochisosama deshita ('I thank you for the meal.') There are also rules for the use of chopsticks: don't stick them upright into a bowl of rice or use them to point at the food. It's a silly mistake that foreigners make. It is also very bad manners to bite or lick your chopsticks. You are also supposed to eat what you are given, including every grain of rice in your bowl.

VOCABULARY Restaurants

A Rewrite the descriptions of the places to eat. Use the words in brackets.

1 At St Germain all the food has lots of butter, cream and eggs. (rich)
   At St Germain *all the food is very rich* .

2 The Gallery restaurant has a view over some beautiful gardens. (looks)
   The Gallery ....

3 Casa Paco always has a lot of people. (packed)
   Casa Paco ....

4 The Olive Tree is decorated in a fashionable way. (decor)
   The Olive Tree ....

5 You can only get seafood at Sea and Surf. (does)
   Sea and Surf ....

B Complete the conversation with the words in the box.

greasy	tough	limited	home-style
huge	inviting	organic	

A: Where do you fancy meeting for lunch?

B: Rob was telling me about a new place in town. It does traditional [1]..................... cooking and the portions are really [2]..................... .

A: Oh, you mean The Cookhouse? They fry everything there, I think, so the food's quite [3]..................... . Someone from work went last weekend and she said her steak was really [4]..................... .

B: OK, let's give that place a miss, then.

A: How about the new cafe at the art gallery? They only do salads and snacks, so the menu's kind of [5]..................... , but the food's all [6]..................... . No chemicals or anything like that.

B: That sounds a bit more [7]..................... .

A: Mmm, a bit healthier, too – I'm watching my weight.

VOCABULARY *over-*

Complete the verbs in the speech bubbles.

1 I think I over *did* the sunbathing yesterday.

2 Sorry, have I over............ ?

3 I think I've over............ the meat.

4 I think we've been over............ .

5 I think I've over............ how much paper we need.

6 I think the iron has over............ .

7 I think I over............ about the parking ticket.

8 Don't show me food. I over............ it at the office party.

GRAMMAR Second conditionals

A **Match the sentence halves.**
1 If I had more time to cook, ...
2 You wouldn't put on weight ......
3 If schools taught basic cookery skills, ...
4 We might buy organic food all the time ......
5 If I cooked you a curry, ...
6 If I wasn't trying to lose weight, ...

a if you didn't eat such fattening food.
b I wouldn't live on ready meals.
c I'd join you for a curry.
d teenagers might be more confident in the kitchen.
e if it wasn't so expensive.
f I think you'd enjoy it.

B **Choose the correct forms.**
1 A: What ¹ *would / will* you do if someone
² *was inviting / invited* you to a restaurant and
then asked you to split the bill?
B: Well, I ³ *might / could* be upset if it
⁴ *was / wasn't* my birthday or something.
C: I ⁵ *didn't / wouldn't* mind. In my country we
always do that.
2 A: Why is that waiter taking so long?
B: Don't be so impatient. No wonder he's a bit slow.
It's packed in here tonight.
A: If I ⁶ *am running / was running* a restaurant,
⁷ *I'd / I'll* give better service than this.
B: That's easy to say. The poor waiter looks
exhausted. If I ⁸ *would be / was* him,
⁹ *I expect / I'd expect* a nice big tip.
A: I don't see why. Just because you're a waiter it
doesn't mean you deserve extra money.
3 A: I don't really know what to have. I might go for
the steak.
B: How hungry are you?
A: Not very.
B: I ¹⁰ *wouldn't / would* have the steak then if
I ¹¹ *would be / were* you. It's huge.
A: OK. I'll have the salad, then. How about drinks?
B: I'll stick with water. If I ¹² *didn't drive / wasn't
driving* home tonight, ¹³ *I could / I can* have a
glass of wine, but I don't want to risk it.

Vocabulary Builder Quiz 8 (*OVB* pp54–55)

**Try the *OVB* quiz for Unit 8. Write your answers in your notebook.
Then check them and record your score.**

A **Tick (✓) the six adjectives that can describe food.**
☐ inviting ☐ mouldy ☐ tender
☐ filling ☐ deserted ☐ generous
☐ starving ☐ tough ☐ full
☐ raw

B **Which texture or taste adjectives ending in -y can go with
these nouns?**
1 .... steak / peaches / oranges
2 .... apples / biscuits / celery
3 .... curry / sauce / stew
4 .... squid / octopus / cheese
5 .... snacks / nuts / crisps

C **Choose the correct words.**
1 Sorry not to finish my lunch. I don't have much
appetite / hungry.
2 The chef is going to *swap / transfer* to another branch of the
restaurant chain.
3 Don't add too much chilli. It will *overreact / overpower* the
other flavours.
4 I'm not sure what to have for the main course. What are you
going to *stick with / go for*?
5 Don't eat too many *sugary / buttery* foods. They are bad for
your teeth.

D **Correct one letter in the underlined words.**
1 I wanted some organic lamb but they were out of <u>stick</u>.
2 Did you know they've <u>binned</u> smoking in all eating places.
3 This stew is really <u>blond</u>. It needs some salt and herbs to add
some flavour.
4 Would you like any <u>site</u> dishes with your main course?
5 The cafe was absolutely <u>picked</u>. It took ages to get served.
6 The flat was really <u>bakc</u> and uninviting when we first moved in.

E **Which word do you need to complete the sentences in
each set?**
1 We stock a wide range of leather .... Electronic .... are
getting cheaper and cheaper all the time. You can buy
imported .... from the market.
2 My favourite .... is Thai green curry. She cooked a
traditional Indian .... We can't serve a meat .... at our
dinner party because she's vegetarian.
3 Would you like to come .... for dinner? I'll pop .... for
coffee later today. When are you going .... to see Mum and
Dad?

Score ___ /25

**Wait a couple of weeks and try the quiz again.
Compare your scores.**

09 HOUSES

VOCABULARY Describing where you live

A These people have answered the question 'What couldn't you live without in your house / flat?' What are they talking about?

1 **Abigail:** I've just bought a sports car, so I have to have somewhere safe to keep it. ....._garage_....

2 **Jo and Lisa:** We need a space to grow our own fruit and vegetables. And we couldn't live without a space for the kids to play safely. b _ _ _ g _ _ _ _ _

3 **Clara:** We use it every day in the summer – it gets so hot here. And it's good exercise. s _ _ _ _ _ _ _ p _ _ _

4 **Reg:** We don't have a garden now but we use the space for all our pot plants. It gives us a lovely view over the city, too. r _ _ _ t _ _ _ _ _ _

5 **Nancy:** I put it on every morning and evening. It's expensive, but I really feel the cold, so I couldn't live without it. g _ _ c _ _ _ _ _ _ h _ _ _ _ _ _

6 **Jake:** I'm a graphic designer and I work from home. I need a space I can use as a studio. b _ _ _ _ _ _ _

B Choose the correct words.

> A six-bedroomed house in a quiet location. The property needs some renovation but has real potential as a lovely family home.
>
> **Key features**
> * a large entrance hall with a beautiful ¹ *tiled / carved* floor
> * an open ² *heating / fire* in each downstairs room
> * a large ³ *roof / loft* that could be converted into a bedroom or home office
> * the main bedroom has a ⁴ *basement / balcony* that looks out over the surrounding countryside
> * beautiful gardens including a lovely ⁵ *square / patio* ideal for sitting and enjoying the view
> * a ⁶ *courtyard / courtroom* surrounded by well-constructed stone buildings

C Complete the conversations with the pairs of words in the box.

run-down / spacious	central / cramped
a shared flat / affordable	conveniently located / bright
newly built / compact	

1 A: I thought you were going to buy your own place. How come you're still living in .... ?
   B: I'm waiting until I can find somewhere .... Everything round here is just so expensive.

2 A: What's your new flat like?
   B: It's great. It's really .... for work – I can walk there in ten minutes – and it's nice and .... , with lots of big windows.

3 A: Why on earth did Max buy that old flat?
   B: I suppose it is a bit .... but it's got five rooms and they are all really ....

4 A: I've gone for one of those .... flats near the hospital. It's good to have a place that doesn't need any work doing to it.
   B: I know where you mean. They look really nice – .... but well designed.

5 A: Shall we have a look at the new houses near the library? It would be good to be in a .... location.
   B: Mmm, I'm not sure. I drove past them last night and they look a bit .... to me. Where would we put all our stuff?

DEVELOPING CONVERSATIONS
Making comparisons

Write the words in brackets in the correct place. There is one extra word each time.

1 The bathroom is .... – it's .... the .... of ours. (half / tiny / twice / size)

2 It's got a nice garden – it's twice .... long as this .... and maybe a bit .... (wider / one / as / size).

3 Those new flats are a bit .... – they're half the size of ours, ... a .... bit smaller. (wide / little / maybe / cramped)

4 Their new house has got a huge kitchen – it's .... the size of .... (twice / enormous / mine / about)

5 The garage is .... – it's .... times the size of .... (yours / about / huge / three)

6 It's got a .... sitting room – it's a .... size to this room, maybe a bit .... (same / bigger / similar / spacious)

READING

A Read the article.
Write the correct names / people.

Who ...

1 started the exchange process with Kyle?   ......
2 got the opportunity to try acting?   ......
3 wanted to create interest in his town?   ......
4 was out of work?   ......
5 visited the house in Kipling?   ......
6 traded to add something to his collection?   ......
7 behaved in a friendly way to Kyle?   ......
8 went to meet all the traders?   ......
9 traded with Kyle to encourage positive attention?   ......

B Complete the tips for finding and sharing a flat. Use the words in **bold** in the article.

People looking for a room

🏠 Register with online flatshare websites to help you in your [1]...................... for a room.

🏠 Don't accept the first room that you see. [2]...................... looking until you find the right place.

🏠 Ask the people in the flat how long the room has been [3]...................... . This is a good way of finding out if there have been any problems.

🏠 Even if the other people in the flat sound friendly over the phone, always meet them [4]...................... .

People with a room to rent

🏠 Give clear information in the advert for the room so that you [5]...................... the right type of person.

🏠 Give the new person in the flat a [6]...................... so that they feel at home quickly.

The man who traded a paperclip for a house

In July 2005, Kyle Macdonald from Montreal set up a series of Internet trades with a red paperclip. A year later and after a total of 14 trades, he exchanged a role in a movie for a house in Kipling, a small town in rural Canada. So, how did this happen?

It all started when Kyle was unemployed and living in Montreal. Instead of putting his CV online, he noticed a red paperclip on his desk and decided to set up a website and trade it on the Internet. His first exchange was with two women in Vancouver, who offered him a pen that looked like a fish. He traded the pen for a doorknob, and then the doorknob for a camping stove. Kyle did all the exchanges **face to face**, as all the traders were more interested in the people than the objects.

After a while, the Canadian media became interested in Kyle's story and the number of daily hits to his website went from about 20 to 100 000. Kyle then said that he intended to keep trading until he got a house. Several exchanges followed until Kyle got a snow globe from the American rock band Kiss. This was exchanged for a minor part in a Hollywood movie. But why would a producer want to exchange a part in a film for a snow globe? Well, the producer, Corbin Bernsen, is one of the biggest collectors of snow globes in the world. Plus, he thought the exchange might be good publicity.

By this time, the development officer of a small town called Kipling had heard about Kyle's **search** for a house. The population of the town had been falling and there were a number of **vacant** houses in the town. The development officer thought that making an exchange with Kyle would be a good way to **attract** tourism. The town bought one of the empty houses and exchanged it with Kyle for the part in the movie.

The first time Kyle and his girlfriend arrived in Kipling, they were given a really **warm welcome**. There were 500 people outside their new house, including the mayor. It was exactly a year after Kyle had made the first trade. The house has now become not only a home for him and his girlfriend but also a tourist attraction. The town held auditions for the role in the movie and a young guy from the local area got the part.

> **Glossary**
>
> **traded:** exchanged something you have for something else; trade (noun)
> **doorknob:** a round handle that you turn to open and close a door
>
> **the media:** radio, TV, newspapers / magazines and the Internet
> **mayor:** the most important elected official in a town / city

VOCABULARY Describing changes

A Match the sentences (1–6) with the graphs (a–f).

1 Interest rates have gone up steadily over the last six months. ...C..

2 The average wage has increased dramatically over the last ten years. ......

3 Unemployment has risen slightly over the last three months. ......

4 The birth rate has dropped dramatically over the last five years. ......

5 House prices have fallen dramatically over the last year. ......

6 The crime rate has gone down steadily over the last three years. ......

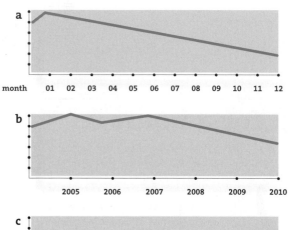

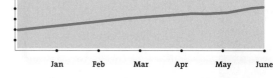

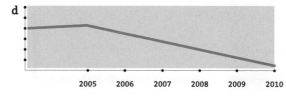

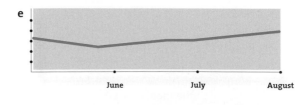

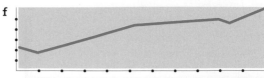

B Complete the answers to the presenter's question. Use the cues in the box. Put the verbs into the present perfect.

> mortgage payments / increase / dramatically
> food prices / go up / a bit
> the cost of energy / drop / steadily
> profits / rise / by about 20%
> property prices / fall / dramatically
> unemployment / go up / a lot

Presenter: We came out onto the streets to ask 'How has the recent financial crisis affected you?' Here are some replies from local people.

Eddie: I haven't worked since I left school. ¹ .... It's very hard to get a job.

Mel: To be honest, we're OK. We have our own business and it's doing well. ² ....

Tara: It's awful. We've just bought our first house but the ³ .... We may have to sell and go back to renting.

Amy: I'm retired but I get a good pension. ⁴ .... but I can still afford to eat well and heat my home.

Charles Oh, please don't ask. I've got three houses to sell but ⁵ .... I could lose a fortune!

Deepak Not too bad, actually. I own a few factories and ⁶ .... over the past few years, so my electricity bills are getting cheaper.

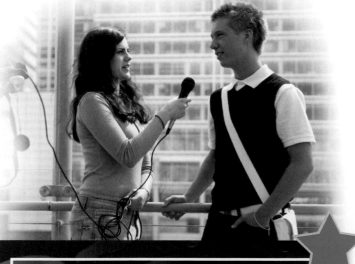

Learner tip

Try to extend the range of language that you use by thinking of different ways of expressing the same idea. Keep a note of examples and how to use them:
Prices have risen dramatically. (often used in writing / more formal speaking)
Prices have gone up a lot. (often used in conversation)

C Choose the correct words.

We bought a pretty little house on the coast a couple of years ago. It was a family home for my wife, our kids and me. At the time there were lots of mortgages at very low interest ¹ *prices / rates*, so we wanted to ² *take / make* advantage of a good deal. Since then, there has been a huge increase ³ *in / of* the number of holiday homes and people buying second homes as ⁴ *profits / investments*. There are so few houses available that there has been a ⁵ *dramatic / dramatically* price rise in all housing. This sounds great but in reality it means that local people can't afford to buy a house in their own area. In the summer, we get thousands of second home owners who come just for short visits. Although they do spend money in the area, they also create problems – they leave litter and do nothing to ⁶ *promote / protect* the local environment. They like having a good time and our village ⁷ *goes / gets* incredibly noisy in the evenings, too. We've tried to ask them to be a bit more considerate but nothing has changed. Like a lot of rural places, I think we need new ways of ⁸ *tackling / dealing* the problem.

LISTENING

A 🔊 **9.1 You are going to hear Paul talking to an estate agent, and then to his sister. Listen to part one and choose the correct information.**
1 The flat is at *29 / 39* Oak Street.
2 The estate agent says the flat is *two / ten* minutes from the tube.
3 He says the flat is *available / affordable*.
4 His name is Mr *Lylle / Kylle*.
5 He *tells / doesn't tell* Paul how much the rent is.

B 🔊 **9.2 Listen to part two. Number the problems with the flat in the order Paul talks about them.**
The flat was:
too expensive ......
tiny ......
very cold ......
in bad condition ......
quite a long way from the underground ......
not very clean ......

PRONUNCIATION Correcting information

Language note sentence stress

We often stress words more strongly when we want to contrast or correct what someone has said or is likely to think.
*I'm not **buying** the flat; I'm **renting** it.*
*The house wasn't very **spa**cious. In fact it was really **cramped**.*

A **Underline the words that contrast or correct.**
1 You couldn't call it compact; it was just cramped.
2 It's wasn't chilly; it was freezing.
3 The agent said it was ten minutes from the tube, but it was more like 20.
4 It was supposed to be affordable but that's just overpriced.

B 🔊 **9.3 Practise saying the sentences in A. Then listen and check.**

C 🔊 **9.4 Match the sentence halves. Then listen and check.**
1 It's too far to walk to the shops, so ......
2 The flat isn't on the first floor; ......
3 We didn't meet the landlord, ...
4 We can't help you move on Friday ......
5 I expected the decor to be quite trendy ......

a just the other tenants.
b but we'll come round at the weekend.
c but it was really old-fashioned.
d you have to get the bus.
e it's in the basement.

D **Practise saying the sentences in C.**

VOCABULARY Describing areas

Write the adjectives in the correct order to complete the opinions.

1 'The area I live in is really ....*lively*........ (ileyvl), with lots of theatres, bars and pubs. The streets are packed with people at weekends, so it can be a bit .... (oysni) but I don't mind that. I used to live in the suburbs and it was just .... (edad) the whole time.'

2 'I was born in quite a .... (ogruh) part of town, with lots of crime and graffiti. It was quite .... (tidyr) and polluted, too. When I made some money, I moved to a .... (atseirednil) area, full of big family houses and nice parks. I suppose you could call it ....' (spho).

3 'We moved out to the country last year and I love living in a beautiful .... (ernge) space. Our nearest neighbours are 12 km away, so we're quite .... (eliotsda). We don't have a local station either, so it isn't very .... (teonevcnin) for transport, but it's worth it for the peace and quiet.'

GRAMMAR
Comparing the past with now

A Correct the underlined mistakes.

1 The pubs and clubs are a lot <u>more rough</u> now.
2 Getting around town is a lot easier <u>that</u> it was before.
3 The air was much <u>most</u> polluted than it is nowadays.
4 Living in the country is <u>somewhere</u> near as good as life in the city.
5 Rents and mortgages are just as high <u>that</u> before.
6 This flat is less <u>noisier</u> than my old place.

B Rewrite the sentences with the words in brackets. Make any necessary changes.

1 Life is more complicated than it was before. (used / be)
   Life ....
2 The air in the town is much cleaner. (much / polluted)
   The air in the town ....
3 House prices are lower than they were. (as / high)
   House prices ....
4 There are a lot more cars than there used to be. (much / traffic)
   There ....
5 There aren't as many businesses in the city centre. (far / fewer)
   There ....
6 There aren't as many tourists as before. (less / tourism)
   There ....

C Victor has written a blog about the changes he has seen in his life. Use one suitable word in each gap to complete his opinions.

○●○○

WHAT'S GOT BETTER

I remember when nearly everyone worked in the local factories. There are a lot [1] ......*more*...... work opportunities now [2] .... there used to [3] .... when I [4] .... a teenager. Health care is [5] .... better now, too, and people are living longer and [6] .... , which is wonderful.

WHAT'S GOT WORSE

I think life has got more and [7] .... stressful because people don't have as [8] .... time as they did [9] .... Fewer and [10] .... young people are choosing to get married, which I think is a shame. In my day, people were [11] .... near as isolated as they [12] .... now, because families tended to stay together.

DEVELOPING CONVERSATIONS
Polite requests

Choose the correct words.

1 A: *Is / Can* it OK if I use some of your milk?
   B: Of course, as long *that / as* you buy some more tomorrow.
2 A: Would you *mind / mine* if I turned the TV over?
   B: *Yes, of course / Not at all* – I'm not watching this anyway.
3 A: I'm a bit short of cash at the moment. *Can / Do* I give you the rent next week?
   B: I'm afraid *not / no*. We all have to pay on time.
4 A: *Can / Would* it be possible to use your computer sometimes?
   B: Of course, *with / within* reason. But please don't spend hours and hours online.
5 A: *Would / Do* it be OK if I have people round for my birthday?
   B: It *depend / depends* how many people – not more than six or eight.
6 A: Do we *have / has* to split all the bills?
   B: No, gas and electricity are included in the rent. *Obviously / Evidently*, you have to pay for any phone calls you make.

DEVELOPING WRITING
A room advert – checking accuracy

A Read the online advert for a room in a shared house. Where would you put the following missing information to make it more complete?

a Large back garden with patio area
b Non-smoker preferred, but not essential
c Room available from 1st September
d spacious sitting room with digital TV
e Supermarkets / takeaways etc are all available locally
f Monthly rent for room: £450

> ● ● ○
>
> http//www.rooms4you.com
>
> 1 ....
> Room available in modern, nicely-decorated house in quite, residential area of York. Approximately 10 miles from city centre, and 15 minutes drive to motorway and train station. Very conveniently location for anyone working at the business park or hospital. 2 ....
>
> The house consists two double bedrooms, two bathrooms (both with electric showers), 3 ...., large, brite kitchen/dining room, laundry room with washing machine and tumble dryer. 4 .... Also unrestricted on-street parking, gas centre heating and broadband access.
>
> I'm an easy-going, professional female, who travels regularly for work. I enjoy cinema, good conversation and relaxing at the end of the day. I'm looking a tidy person who isn't too nosy, possibly a young professional or post-graduate student. 5 ....
>
> 6 .... All bills are included, except telephone.
>
> Interested? Please contact me via the website.

B Correct the underlined mistakes in the advert.

C Imagine you have a room to rent in your house / flat. Write an advert (120–150 words) for the room. Include the information in the checklist and check your work carefully.

- when the room is available
- a description of the area
- a description of the house and what's in it
- a brief personal description
- a brief description of the type of person you are looking for
- the rent and what's included

Vocabulary Builder Quiz 9 (OVB pp34–36)

Try the *OVB* quiz for Unit 9. Write your answers in your notebook. Then check them and record your score.

A Cross out the adjective that isn't possible in the context.

1 This area is just too (touristy / built-up / posh) for me. I'm used to living in the middle of nowhere.
2 A few years ago this part of town was quite (dead / green / run-down) but it's improved a lot since then.
3 We've knocked down the wall to make a really (enormous / separate / spacious) room.
4 The houses in (residential / compact / affordable) areas always sell very quickly.

B Which six of these situations are a problem / negative?

The roof is leaking.
The bathroom floor has just been tiled.
The value of our house has doubled.
There's a shortage of affordable housing.
There were hardly any volunteers for the clean-up campaign.
The building project has gone over budget.
They've finally paid off their mortgage.
The central heating needs fixing.
The graffiti in the area put off potential buyers.

C Match the sentence halves.

1 Why don't you have a
2 Why are you taking
3 House prices have fallen
4 Interest rates will rise
5 What is the root
6 We need to tackle

a dramatically in the last year.
b go at repairing the light yourself.
c the housing problem.
d out a loan if you're already overdrawn?
e of the problem?
f steadily in the next six months.

D Which words that are both verbs and nouns can complete these sentences?

1 They've just put up the .... on our flat. I don't know why more people don't .... instead of having a mortgage.
2 Our main .... is to pay off our mortgage quickly. These plans .... to provide local people with better housing.
3 There's been a dramatic .... in unemployment. It's estimated that prices will .... by two per cent.
4 How much .... do you think the company made? Politicians shouldn't .... from being in power.

E What form of the words in brackets do you need to complete the text?

They're holding local [1] (elect) in my area soon. All of the candidates have promised to make [2] (improve) to the town. I hope they will come up with some [3] (innovation) ideas for transport. The town isn't very well [4] (connection) with other areas. It would take a lot of [5] (invest) to develop the links but it would be well worth it.

Score ___ /25

**Wait a couple of weeks and try the quiz again.
Compare your scores.**

VOCABULARY Films, exhibitions and plays

A Put the words in the correct category.

drama	photography	comedy	installation
soundtrack	sculpture	portrait	sculptor
special effects	plot	tragedy	still life
historical play	video artist	landscape	

- Aspects of a film
- Exhibitions
- Types of painting
- Types of play

B Complete the conversations with the words in the box. There is one extra word each time

lighting	gig	comedy	audience

1 A: Did you enjoy the .... ?
   B: Yes and no. The stage .... was amazing – they used loads of different colours – and the sound was great. But the band only played for 45 minutes. Half of the .... asked for their money back.

acting	soundtrack	director	scenery	costumes

2 A: That wasn't the best play I've ever seen. Remind me, who was the .... ?
   B: Karl Mitchell. He must be quite inexperienced because the .... wasn't very believable.
   A: You're right. The best thing about it was the .... – I loved all those long, silk dresses.
   B: Mmm, the .... was pretty good, too. It really looked like they were in Paris.

thriller	special effects	trailer
romantic comedy	horror films	

3 A: I saw a .... for *Dance of the Vampires*. Do you fancy going?
   B: Er, I'm not really into ...., actually. I usually go for a nice ...., where the couple end up getting married.
   A: Well, there isn't much else on at the moment apart from a spy .... set in the Middle East.

painting	landscape	painter	abstract

4 A: Look at this. Aren't the colours fantastic? And the .... style is really unusual. Do you know who the .... is?
   B: No idea. It's all a bit too .... for me. I like pictures to look like real people and objects.

C Write questions for the answers.

1 A: ....
   B: There's loads on just now – a music festival, an art installation at the museum and a new version of a Shakespeare play.

2 A: ....
   B: It's a collection of black and white photography.

3 A: ....
   B: It's a play about life in New York in the 1920s.

4 A: ....
   B: At the new City Gallery, on Princes Street.

5 A: ....
   B: They've got a late-night showing at 11:30 on Friday and Saturday.

6 A: ....
   B: A couple of new actors I haven't heard of before.

DEVELOPING CONVERSATIONS
Explaining where things are

Choose the correct words.

1 A: Do you know where the mosque is?
  B: No, sorry I don't think I do.
  C: You know the main square? Well, Charles Street is one of the roads ¹ *off / of* there. If you're ² *come / coming* down the road away from the square, there's a turning on the right. The mosque is about ³ *halfway / half time* down that road, on the right.

2 A: Hello, 239816.
  B: Hello, I'm trying to deliver a parcel to you but I can't find the address. I'm on Market Street.
  A: Holly Lane is pedestrianised so you can't drive round, but it isn't far to walk. If you've got your ⁴ *turn / back* to the main square, you take the second left. Follow the road round and number 19 is ⁵ *straight / right* on the corner.

3 A: Where are you? I thought we were meeting at the bus station. I'm right ⁶ *in front / opposite* of the main entrance now.
  B: Sorry, I meant the train station. I'm in the car park ⁷ *by / at* the back.
  A: OK, well, let's meet at the restaurant. You know where it is, don't you?
  B: Is it the one on Marshal Road?
  A: No, it's the ⁸ *near / next* turning down from there. It's only about five minutes' walk.

4 A: Sorry I'm late. My train was delayed, Where are you now?
  B: I'm outside the art gallery. When you come ⁹ *out / off* of the station, go up Carlton Road ¹⁰ *between / towards* the main square. You'll see a big statue in the middle. If you're ¹¹ *front / facing* the statue, the gallery is on your left.

LISTENING

🔊10.1 Listen to six short dialogues. Choose the correct answers, a, b or c.

1 What do they decide to do?
  a go out for dinner
  b go to the cinema
  c stay in
2 Which showing of the film do they choose?
  a 4:30 p.m.
  b 7 p.m.
  c 9 p.m.
3 What are the people doing?
  a looking at paintings
  b taking photos
  c watching a video
4 What do they think is the best thing about the film?
  a the plot
  b the soundtrack
  c the special effects
5 Where do they decide to meet?
  a in the main square
  b at the lady's house
  c at the station
6 Where is the ice rink?
  a to the right of the internet cafe
  b down from the station
  c facing the internet café

PRONUNCIATION Same sound or different?

A Are the letters in bold the same sound (S) or different (D)?

1 Do you **fa**ncy going tonight? / Come and look at this landsc**a**pe. ......
2 There's nothing **o**n. / That always used to be quite p**o**sh. ......
3 What other sh**o**wings are there? / That part of town is a bit rough n**o**wadays. ......
4 He does **v**ideos as well. / No silly special **e**ffects for a change. ......
5 It's the second time I've been to this exhibit**io**n. / He does ph**o**tography as well. ......
6 Is it **r**ight opposite the Internet cafe? / What about in the m**ai**n square? ......

B 🔊10.2 Listen and check. Practice saying the sentences.

VOCABULARY Describing what's on

A Complete the opinions with the correct form of the adjectives in brackets.

1 I thought it was .... (amaze)! I loved the acting, the plot, the photography – everything!

2 The place looked nice but the portions were just tiny. I don't think I'll go again – I'm not that impressed by .... (trend) decor.

3 The first half wasn't great and then Harper scored a .... (spectacle) try just before half time.

4 The bar owner had given us some free tickets to see the salsa. But when we got there, there were no locals at all and half the performers were English. It was all a bit .... (tourist) for me.

5 It was OK but there was an .... (credible) number of people there. You couldn't see any of the sculptures very clearly.

6 The review said it had a .... (marvel) cast of young actors, but the best part for me was when the final curtain came down.

B What are the people in exercise A talking about?

a play	..6..	a film	......
a dance show	......	a rugby match	......
a restaurant	......	an exhibition	......

C Read the opinions and complete the adjectives.

1 The play was so d _ _ _ I fell asleep halfway through.

2 I've never had such a t _ _ _ _ _ _ meal. What a rip-off!

3 Why did I spend £10 on a ticket to see that d _ _ _ _ _ _ film? Never again!

4 Wow! What a b _ _ _ _ _ _ _ _ performance! I wish I could sing like that.

5 I just didn't get it. The story was much too w _ _ _ _ for my taste.

6 She's just t _ _ _ _ _ _ _ ! I hope she wins an Oscar for her acting.

D Match the sentence halves

1 I haven't eaten at the new steak house yet,
2 I haven't seen the new James Bond film,
3 I haven't heard the new Rolling Stones CD yet,
4 I haven't been to the modern art exhibition,
5 I haven't tried the new sports centre yet,
6 I haven't bought anything at the new department store yet,

a but it's supposed to have some real bargains.
b but the equipment is supposed to be brilliant.
c but the special effects are supposed to be quite dull.
d but the images are supposed to be quite weird.
e but the food's supposed to be delicious.
f but the songs are supposed to be a bit disappointing.

DEVELOPING CONVERSATIONS
Why you do not want to do things

A Cross out one extra word in each sentence.

1 It sounds a bit of too trendy for me.
2 I'm not really in the mood right for that kind of thing.
3 It is sounds a bit too weird for me.
4 It's not really my kind of any thing.
5 I don't really feel to like it.
6 It looks a bit too touristy for me self.

B Use the corrected sentences from exercise A to complete the conversations.

1 A: Do you fancy going for a walk?
 B: .... I'm a bit tired, actually.

2 A: Shall we sign up for tango classes as the dance studio?
 B: Sorry, but .... I've got two left feet.

3 A: There's a new club just opened in town. Apparently, all the models and designers go there. Do you fancy it?
 B: Not really. ....

4 A: Have you heard about the art installation at the museum? They have interactive images of inside the human body. Shall I get tickets?
 B: Erm, not for me thanks. .... I prefer traditional paintings.

5 A: Have a look at this holiday resort in Jamaica. You can get an all-inclusive deal with your hotel, food and drinks, everything.
 B: .... I'm into quieter places.

6 A: There's a new Swedish film on in town. It's supposed to be a bit heavy but with amazing photography.
 B: Sorry, but .... I need cheering up.

READING

A Read the article quickly. How does the writer feel about people who wear special clothes to go to the cinema?

a a bit surprised but not positive or negative
b annoyed and very critical
c amused and very impressed

B Read the article again. Decide if these sentences about the text are true or false, or if the article doesn't say.

1 The writer doesn't tend to dress up when she goes to see a film.
2 Some filmgoers have a similar reaction in a cinema as people often do in the theatre.
3 The writer wished she could join in one of the *Sex and the City* themed parties.
4 Nearly all film audiences who dress up are young and female.
5 Film audiences used to get annoyed if people made a noise during a cinema film.
6 The writer understands why people try to express their liking for a film directly to the cast.
7 The writer hopes that all films in the future will have their own dress code.

PUT ON YOUR BALLGOWN – WE'RE GOING TO THE CINEMA

What do you wear to the cinema? If you're anything like me, then the answer is a pair of jeans, and a top or a jumper. But both you and I are behind the times, because there is a new type of film fan out there: they dress up to look like their favourite stars, they treat going to the cinema like a party, and respond to the cast of the film as if they had been in a play.

I witnessed this for myself when *Sex and the City* was released in UK cinemas. I turned up in my usual top and jeans and found myself surrounded by young women in party dresses and high heels. They were all paying respect to their favourite characters in the film. Apparently, some groups of women even took it further by organizing a whole evening of events – make-up at a beauty salon, cocktails before and after the film, and themed parties related to the *Sex and the City* lifestyle.

Later the same year, *Mamma Mia!* came out and it was the turn of the older film fans to wear their favourite fashions from the 1970s and sing along to the Abba soundtrack. And it's not just girls who love romantic comedies who get involved; male fans of the *Batman* series of films were also seen in full costume for a screening of *The Dark Knight*.

It seems that the audience reaction during a film isn't the same as it used to be. Until a few of years ago, all the interacting was done by the actors on the screen. If anyone made a noise when opening some sweets or having a drink, the people nearby would respond with a loud 'Sshh!' Nowadays, some people applaud and shout when the film starts, cheer when their favourite character appears, and even give a standing ovation at the end if they've really loved the movie.

You have to admit that this is a strange thing to do when the actors can't hear you! And of course, it doesn't happen with all types of audience. A tense thriller or moving account of war is unlikely to create spontaneous shouts and applause.
But there does seem to be a trend for lighter films to attract an interactive audience. Maybe film-makers will pick up on this and there will be a dress code for every popular movie that is released …

Glossary

dress up: put on special clothes
applaud: show you enjoyed something by hitting the palms of your hands together
cheer: give a loud shout of approval

C Match the sentence halves.

1 She was amazing; the audience gave
2 Have you seen any good films or plays? I'm completely behind
3 She didn't win an Oscar until her seventies but at least the industry paid
4 I know you like this song, but do you have to sing
5 I think I saw Johnny Depp at the airport but he was surrounded
6 Films seem to be getting more and more violent. Why do directors take it
7 Surfing the Net is a good way of picking
8 Don't wait for Marcus. He always turns

a the times with what's on at the moment.
b up late and you don't want to miss the start.
c along to it every time it comes on?
d by security and fans so it was hard to see.
e up on new films and CDs.
f further in every film they make?
g her a standing ovation which lasted minutes.
h respect to her in the end.

VOCABULARY Describing an event

Choose the correct words.

1. A: How was the film?
   B: It was OK, but a bit *overpriced / overrated*. I don't think the director is as terrific as everyone's been *saying / telling*.
   C: Oh, I loved it. It was so *moving / scary*. When the young girl died, I was in *crying / tears*.
   A: It must be popular. I tried to get a ticket for the late showing and it was completely sold *up / out*.

2. A: I didn't see you after the gig.
   B: No, I left halfway *through / down*.
   A: How come?
   B: I thought they were *rubbish / rough* – just really dull.
   A: You're kidding. I thought it was amazing. There was such a good *atmosphere / scenery*. I enjoyed the music, the light show, *all / everything*.
   B: In that case, you should buy their latest CD. It's supposed to have a lot of songs from the live tour.

3. A: Have you tried the new club on Dale Street?
   B: Yeah, and I wouldn't bother going if I were you. It's very *abstract / trendy* – full of young, beautiful people. I was wearing jeans and I felt a bit out of *place / mood*.
   A: What about the music?
   B: Pretty dreadful. It was mainly catchy pop songs, so the dance floor was *stuck / packed* with teenagers. It was boiling *warm / hot* and I was sweating like *crazily / crazy,* even though I wasn't dancing much.

4. A: Everyone's raving about the new exhibition at the modern art gallery. What's so good about it?
   B: It's one of the most interesting things I've seen in ages. The paintings are *worried / weird*. I can't really describe them or say *what / why* I like them. They're just different.
   A: Mm, I'd better go along and have a look for myself.

GRAMMAR The future in the past

A Rewrite the sentences to refer to future plans made in the past.

1. I am going to meet some friends at the cinema.
   She said ....

2. I'll get the theatre tickets online.
   He promised ....

3. I don't think the gig will be very good.
   She didn't think ....

4. I won't be late for the party, I promise.
   He promised ....

5. The gig will probably finish at about 11.30.
   The manager said ....

6. I think all the clubs are going to be packed.
   She thought that ....

B Complete the conversations with the correct form of the pairs of verbs in the box.

going to / ring	wouldn't / spend
might / come	supposed / arrive

1. A: You're half an hour late – what happened?
   B: Sorry, I .... you but I couldn't get a signal on my mobile.

2. A: Is Annie joining us for a drink?
   B: I'm not sure. She said she .... if she could get away from work.

3. A: You .... at the client's office at 9:30. What happened?
   B: I'm really sorry. I got struck in traffic.

4. A: Why are you in such a bad mood?
   B: You promised you .... so much time at work but you are at the office 24/7.

DEVELOPING WRITING
Emails – arranging to go out

A Complete the emails with the words in the box. There is one extra word each time.

B Number the emails in A in the order they were sent.

C Write a series of short emails.

> Write a message inviting a classmate to go out for the evening.

↓

> Refuse the invitation in a polite way.

↓

> Persuade your classmate to come with you.

↓

> Agree. Ask when and where to meet.

↓

> Reply and give the relevant information.

Learner tip

Writing notes and emails to other people in your class is a great way of practising real English. If possible, exchange the emails in exercise C with a classmate and reply to his / her messages. You can do this online or on a single sheet of paper.

A get meet coming know

You ¹...................... the tourist information place? If you're ²...................... down the road away from it, the arts centre is about halfway down, on the left. I'll ³...................... two tickets for Saturday. It starts at 7:30.

B tickets reservations reviews excuses dull

Don't be so boring! This play isn't heavy or ¹...................... – it's funny. It's got some really good ²...................... , so you might be pleasantly surprised. Anyway, you've been promising to come out with me for ages, so no more ³...................... . I'll even buy the ⁴...................... if you say yes.

C way come do make

OK, OK. I'll ¹...................... with you. It will ²...................... a change to do something different. Where is this new centre, by the ³...................... ?

D better nice kind ever

It's ¹...................... of you to ask me, but it isn't really my ²...................... of thing. I went to a Russian play recently and it was one of the worst things I've ³...................... seen. Sorry!

E fancy right on supposed out

There's a comedy play on at the new arts centre in town. I haven't been yet but it's ¹...................... to be great fun. Do you ²...................... going? It's about a guy who leads a double life – half the time he's a teacher and the rest he's a spy. It's ³...................... until the 17th, so this is the last weekend. I can't remember who's in it, but it could be a good night ⁴...................... .

Vocabulary Builder Quiz 10 (*OVB* pp38–40)

Try the *OVB* quiz for Unit 10. Write your answers in your notebook. Then check them and record your score.

A Which words in each set do you need to complete the sentences?

| audience crowd squad cast |

1 All the actors in the .... performed brilliantly.
2 The average age of the .... for this show is about 23.

| portrait landscape sculpture still life |

3 Painting a self .... must be very difficult.
4 He turned a lump of stone into a brilliant ....

| plot soundtrack subtitles trailer |

5 Have you seen the .... for the new Coen Brothers film?
6 They adapted the film from the novel but they changed the .... quite a lot.

B Complete the nouns that end in *-ion*.

1 That's brilliant news about your promotion, ...ions!
2 Can you help me put up the ....ions for Dan's party?
3 Thousand of people went on the anti-war ....ion.
4 That poor family. They lost all their ....ions when their house burnt down.
5 Can I make a ....ion? Why don't we have a break and continue the meeting after lunch?
6 We have no ....ion but to sell the company. There's nothing else we can do.

C Find the error in the sentence below and correct it.

1 I'm not very seen on modern art.
2 I'll give you a gift to the station if you like.
3 She burst into fears when she heard the news.
4 The late slowing of the film doesn't finish until after midnight.
5 Take the next burning on the left.
6 He always sails to understand what I'm trying to say.

D Which adjectives from *OVB* 10 can replace the underlined words.

1 His new film is really <u>strange</u>. It's nearly impossible to follow the story.
2 I felt really <u>uncomfortable</u> in my jeans when everyone else was dressed up.
3 There was an <u>unbelievable</u> crowd at the opening night of the play.
4 She lives in a really <u>nice</u> part of town, right by the main park.
5 They'd built the most <u>amazing</u> scenery for the new production of *Swan Lake*.
6 We had the most <u>awful</u> meal while we were in Paris.
7 For the <u>real</u> taste of Spain, come to Casa Paco.

Score ____ /25

Wait a couple of weeks and try the quiz again. Compare your scores.

VOCABULARY Animals

A 🔊 **11.1 Listen to the sounds and complete the names.**

1 b _ear_
2 p _ _ _ _ _ _
3 d _ _ _ _ _ _
4 w _ _ _
5 c _ _ _
6 w _ _ _ _

B Complete the descriptions with the words in the box.

crocodiles	deer	lizards
eagles	squirrels	cockroaches

1 .... are found in Asia, the Americas and Europe. The majority have large, bushy tails.
2 .... are a large group of reptiles found in all continents except Antarctica. They range in size from a few centimetres long to nearly three metres.
3 .... live in a wide range of environments around the world. About 30 species of this insect are seen as harmful pests.
4 .... are large birds of prey found all over the world. They are often used as national symbols.
5 .... are large aquatic reptiles that live in the tropical areas of Africa, Asia, north and south America, and Australia.
6 .... are quite large, four-legged mammals. The males have large horns.

DEVELOPING CONVERSATIONS
Helping to tell stories

Number the lines in the correct order.

1 Well I was driving home from the office when I suddenly
saw a deer in the road. ......
I guess it had come out of the forest that stretches along the side of the road. ......
The poor animal looked really scared and confused. ......
So what happened in the end? ......
You'll never guess what happened last night. ......
Well, the police and wildlife officers were going to tranquilise it, but they couldn't shoot at it because there was still a lot of traffic around. As far as I know, they haven't caught it yet. ......
Seriously? In the middle of all the traffic? ......
But what was it doing there? ......
Go on. What? ......
Yeah! It was a huge animal, with really big antlers
It was actually a bit scary. I thought it might run into one of the cars. ......

2 Nobody knows. But it had hidden so deeply inside the engine that they had to take it apart to get the cat out. It had been there for a week without food or water and the guy had driven 300 miles! ......
Did you hear about that cat that spent a week stuck in a car engine? ......
No, it was amazing. It just had a few minor burns on its fur. ......
So what happened in the end? ......
No, what was that? ......
The guy gave the cat back to his neighbour. Apparently, it was fine, despite what had happened. ......
I think it was in Austria. This guy heard a sound coming from his Mercedes so he looked under the bonnet and found his neighbour's cat. ......
But what was it doing there? ......
Seriously? Not hurt or anything? ......

GRAMMAR -ing clauses

A Complete the sentences with the correct form of the pairs of verbs in the box.

bark / sing	live / run	learn / catch
circle / dive	crawl / bite	lie / sit

1 The sky was empty and then suddenly we saw an eagle .... and then .... to catch its prey.
2 I'll never go trekking again. I couldn't stand the scorpions .... all over the place and the insects .... me.
3 It was impossible to sleep. There was a dog .... all night and then the birds .... from 5 a.m.
4 Max is crazy about animals. Last time I saw him there was a snake .... round his shoulders and a parrot .... on his head.
5 We went on a safari. It was amazing to see the animals .... in their own environment and .... free.
6 I watched a great documentary last night. It showed young tigers .... to hunt and .... small deers.

LISTENING

🔊 **11.2** **Listen to Mark talking to his friend Amy about a trip to a safari park. Number the pictures in the correct order.**

PRONUNCIATION Same pronunciation, different spelling

Write the correct spelling for the pairs of words in phonetics.

1 I'd been promising to take a friend's /sʌn/. ....
   I decided to open the /sʌn/ roof. ....
2 The /ˈweðə/ was great. ....
   Do you know /ˈweðə/ you'll be allowed to go back? ....
3 It didn't /breɪk/ anything. ....
   I had to /breɪk/ quickly. ....
4 There were /red/ deer and squirrels, things like that. ....
   You should have /red/ the rules. ....
5 I said I was going to /raɪt/ to the manager. ....
   That can't be /raɪt/, can it? ....
6 We had to /weɪt/ ages for it to move. ....
   The /weɪt/ of the animal had left a big dent. ....

> **Learner tip**
>
> There are a number of words in English that have the same pronunciation but different spelling:
> *Look at that beautiful* **deer.**
> *Oh,* **dear**. *My cat has gone missing.*
> When you are listening, use the context to help you understand which word is being used. When you are writing, check you have used the correct spelling.

GRAMMAR Passives

A Complete the quiz by putting the verbs in brackets into a passive form. Then choose the correct answers, A, B or C.

What do you know about the natural world?

① How much of the Earth's surface .... (cover) in water?
A about 20%   B about 70 %   C about 90%

② Which area .... sometimes .... (know) as the 'lungs of the earth'?
A the Brazilian rainforest   B the River Nile   C the Arctic

③ Which regions .... (know) for 'auroras' (natural displays of light in the sky)?
A rainforests   B deserts   C polar regions

④ How many plants species .... (use) in medicines worldwide?
A 100–200   B 1,000–2,000   C 10,000 – 20,000

⑤ Which plants .... (develop) over the centuries for use as painkillers?
A poppy and willow   B garlic and tea   C rice and sugar cane

⑥ Which animals .... (breed) in zoos in Poland in the last century to stop them becoming extinct?
A wolves   B deer   C bison

⑦ Which animal .... (adopt) as the logo for the WWF (World Wildlife Fund) in the 1960s?
A panda   B tiger   C whale

⑧ What is the main reason that many species of animal .... (threaten) with extinction?
A hunting and trading   B destruction of habitats   C lack of food

B Rewrite the sentences in the passive.

1 They are building a new shopping centre in the centre of town.
A ....
....

2 They smuggled the diamonds out of the country in bags of sugar.
The ....
....

3 They were repairing the photocopier all yesterday morning.
The ....
....

4 They grade students according to their age and ability.
Students ....
....

5 They have given all civil servants a pay rise.
All ....
....

6 They will interview the new president on live TV.
The ....
....

READING

A Read the article quickly and write the names of the plants on the timeline.

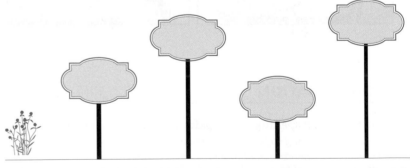

Past   Present

B Read the article again and match the questions (1–8) to the correct text (A–D).

Which plant
1 was sometimes dangerous to humans?   ......
2 is used in cosmetics?   ....
3 has been adapted a lot over time?   ......
4 has been important in spreading knowledge?   ......
5 has uses in areas of technology?   ......
6 was first tested by a single person?   ......
7 is grown across different continents?   ....
8 has influenced English vocabulary?   ......

Plants for life

If you were asked, 'What has made the biggest contribution to human development?', you might say 'computers' or 'cars', rather than 'cotton' or 'wheat'. But throughout history plants have played a vital role. Here are just a few examples of 'hero' plants:

A Cotton

No one knows exactly where cotton originated but the earliest pieces of cotton cloth were found in Mexico and are about 7000 years old. Now more cotton is grown than any other natural fibre in the world, in a business that is worth billions of dollars a year. Top exporters include the USA, Brazil and India. The use of cotton in clothes is well-known but in fact all parts of the cotton plant are useful – the seed to make oils for soap and margarine, and the part around the seed for making gunpowder, nail polish and plastics!

B Wheat

Wheat used to make bread originated about 10–15,000 years ago and thousands of years of plant breeding has led to the modern, high-production varieties used today. Now wheat provides more food for more people worldwide than any other crop. It is grown in every continent, except Antarctica, because varieties have been produced to suit different climates. It is used in the Western diet for bread and pasta, but also in Asia to make another staple food – noodles. Other uses for wheat include hand cleaners, soap and shampoo.

C Papyrus

Papyrus was probably first used to make paper in Egypt about 4000 BC. The word 'paper' itself comes from 'papyrus'. The plant is a distant relative of cotton and is grown in Africa, Madagascar and the southern Mediterranean. Historically, the plant had huge importance. It was the first product that was strong enough to hold written information but was also light enough to be portable. This meant that important information could be written down, stored and exchanged. Papyrus is also now used to improve soil conditions in Africa and in the production of biofuels.

D Foxglove

The foxglove was regularly used in herbal medicine but could be fatal because parts of the plant are poisonous. In the 18th century, a Scottish doctor discovered that the plant contained an ingredient that had a powerful effect on the heart. This chemical (digitalin) is still used in modern medicine to control a patient's heart rate. The foxglove has an attractive flower and is found throughout Britain and in western and southern Europe. Digitalin is just one example of how the plant world has benefited human health across the centuries.

Glossary

fibre: a type of cloth or other material
gunpowder: a substance used for masking explosions
crop: a plant grown for food
biofuel: fuel produced from plant material

C Choose the correct words.

Plants have played a [1] *vital / fatal* role throughout human history. They have [2] *made / done* a contribution to business, medicine, food, art, and even architecture. Thanks to early travellers, plants that [3] *created / originated* in one area were transported to be grown in different places. Seeds are one of the most [4] *possible / portable* parts of a plant, allowing [5] *crops / breeds* like rice to start life in Asia and then be introduced to the Americas and Europe. Plants even [6] *made / had* an effect on politics – historically, the country that controlled the spice trade was the most powerful in the world.

VOCABULARY Keeping pets

A Complete the texts with the words in the boxes.

mess	jump	lick	looking after
exercise	puppies	leftovers	dry food
scratch	to an enormous size		

1 I'm not very keen on dogs. They need such a lot of
¹ .... People buy cute little
² .... without realising they will
grow, sometimes ³ .... Even
little dogs need a lot of ⁴ .... and
you have to walk them every day. Some people feed
their dogs ⁵ .... from the family
meals, but you also need to buy tinned and
⁶ .... , which can be quite
expensive. The worst thing for me is the
⁷ .... they can make of your
house. My sister's dogs, for example,
⁸ .... her furniture, but she
doesn't seem to mind. They also
⁹ .... on any visitors who come
to the door and even ¹⁰ .... their
hands if they try to stroke them. It's just horrible!

smelly	outside	playful	hold
food	litter tray	kittens	big
attention	aggressive	noise	play

2 There's an elderly lady down our street who must own
about 30 cats. They are all different sizes, some have
grown quite ¹ .... and others are
still tiny ² .... The little ones
stay in the house but I think the lady keeps the adult
cats ³ .... I don't think they get
very much ⁴ .... because they
don't seem to like people very much. They become
quite ⁵ .... , so you can't
⁶ .... or
⁷ .... with them. They are always
fighting and they make an awful
⁸ .... when they do. All those
animals need a lot of ⁹ .... and I
saw the old lady carrying a huge bag of tins back from
the supermarket one day. I offered to help her but I
have to admit her house was a bit
¹⁰ .... I don't think she cleaned
the ¹¹ .... very often. It was a
shame because I love cats and the little kittens were
really cute and ¹² .... I just
think it was too much for one person to look after.

B Choose the correct words.

A beginners' guide to keeping pet snakes

There is a common myth that all snakes are dangerous or
even ¹ *poison / poisonous*. The truth is that snakes are a lot
less ² *demanding / demanded* than other animals and can
make good family pets.
- It's important to buy snakes as ³ *babies / eggs* so that they
  become used to their environment as they grow.
- Find out what will be the final *adult* size of the snake –
  even smaller species can grow ⁴ *up / to* about 1.5 metres.
- The best place to keep a snake is in a special
  ⁵ *tank / cage* called a vivarium.
- Don't forget to clean the vivarium ⁶ *regular / regularly*.
- Snakes have quite a simple
  diet of ⁷ *mice / mouses*.
  Don't worry – these
  don't need to be alive,
  but can be bought …

VOCABULARY Forming words

A Complete the sentences with the correct form of the words in brackets.

1 The police are carrying out .... (investigate) into the
smuggling of endangered species.
2 Many species of animal are .... (threat) by climate
change.
3 The tiger is in danger of .... (extinct).
4 I went on a demonstration against the .... (destroy)
of an area of forest.
5 I hate seeing lions and tigers in zoos – I think all animals
should have their .... (free).
6 We need to start listening to the .... (warn) about
protecting the rainforest.
7 My dad's guide dog is so important to him. It really helps him
maintain his .... (independent).

**B Complete the table with a noun or verb form of the words in the
box. Some can go in more than one place.**

direct	length	spell	combine	correct	bore
imagine	meet	relevant	convenient	fright	king

e + -ation	+ -dom	+ -en
+ -ing	**+ -ion**	**t + -ce**

DEVELOPING WRITING
A blog – giving an opinion

A Choose the correct words.

http//www.keepingpets.com/blog

I'm just not an animal person

I have nothing ¹ *opposite / against* animals in general and I really enjoy wildlife programmes on TV. Working animals like guide dogs are very important, of course, but I can't see the ² *point / place* of keeping pets. To ³ *me / mine*, they just ⁴ *take / make* a mess and cost you a lot of money. And some pet owners ⁵ *treat / look* their animals like children, dressing them up and feeding them the best meat or fish. It's just crazy! ⁶ *That / What* really gets me is when people set up a blog 'written' by their dog or cat. Why do they pretend that an animal has opinions to share with the rest of the world? As I ⁷ *see / think* it, if you want to communicate, talk to a person, not a pet. Posted by DrPhil at 21:32, *1 comment*

I couldn't live without my pets

Sorry, Dr Phil, I ⁸ *couldn't / don't* disagree more! I have three cats and two dogs and I ⁹ *take / get* a lot out of keeping them. I don't spoil them or treat them like humans, but they ¹⁰ *hold / mean* a lot to me. What I love about them is the ¹¹ *fact / right* that they are very loyal. I live alone and so I don't have much contact with people day to day. Looking after my animals is an important part of each day. ¹² *Don't forget / remind* that there are a lot of people out there just ¹³ *as / like* me. I ¹⁴ *take / agree* your point about animals 'writing' blogs, though, that is very silly! Posted by naturequeen at 21:59, *2 comments*

Language note adding emphasis

Sentences that begin with a clause starting with *What* add emphasis to a subject or object. Compare:
The way she treats her pets really annoys me.
What really annoys me is the way she treats her pets.

B Write a reply (120–150 words) to one of the opinions in exercise A. Include your overall opinion on keeping pets, reasons for your opinions and examples from your own experience.

Vocabulary Builder Quiz 11 (*OVB* pp42–44)

Try the *OVB* quiz for Unit 11. Write your answers in your notebook. Then check them and record your score.

A Match 1–5 and a–e.
1 litter a investigation
2 global b industry
3 speed c tray
4 police d camera
5 construction e warming

B Which word do you need to complete the sentences in each pair?
1 At one .... I thought the dog was going to attack me.
We've reached the .... where we have to make a decision.
2 I found my keys .... the bed.
What are you wearing .... your coat?
3 Don't let your dog run .... in the park.
Why did you set the birds ....?
4 Zoos play an important .... in breeding programmes.
What's his .... in the government?

C Choose the correct words.
1 Be careful. The cat might *scratch / stroke* you.
2 Don't forget to change the water in the fish *cage / tank*.
3 You're not allowed to walk on the *grass / bush* here.
4 Huge areas of natural *habitat / inhabitants* are under threat.
5 I met a man who *species / breeds* racehorses.
6 The *destruction / extinction* of the rainforest is a serious issue.

D Complete the sentences using the correct form of the verbs in the box.

ban suspend release arrest threaten move

1 Their first CD .... next month.
2 All the gang members .... just after the robbery.
3 Currently a lot of workers .... with losing their jobs.
4 He .... from driving for two years after he was caught speeding.
5 Everyone .... when they heard the sad news.
6 All services on the underground .... from 6 a.m. tomorrow.

E Find words that are both nouns and verbs to complete the sentences.
1 My baby sister has just learned to ....
My friends all went on a pub .... last weekend.
2 It's a real .... from my house to where I work.
They're planning to .... across the Andes.
3 There has been a wide .... for the missing money.
Why do the staff always .... my bags when I go through security?
4 It's illegal to .... rhinos and elephants.
The .... for the gang of smugglers has moved to Amsterdam.

Score ____ /25

Wait a couple of weeks and try the quiz again.
Compare your scores.

12 PEOPLE I KNOW

VOCABULARY Describing character

A Read the opinions and complete the puzzle with the correct character adjectives. Then find the hidden word.

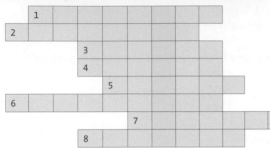

1 Once he's made his mind up, he won't ever change it. He's just so ....

2 We weren't expecting it, but dad paid for our honeymoon. It was so .... of him.

3 The new guy at work is so .... it's hard to get any work done.

4 My niece is quite a .... child – she seems good at most subjects at school.

5 My little cousin is so .... – she gets everything that she asks for.

6 We're an odd couple. I get upset and stressed quite easily but my husband is really ....

7 I wish he would learn to relax. He's just so ....

8 I'm afraid I had to send Matthew home. He was being so .... at the party that the other children couldn't enjoy it.

> **Language note** *it was (kind) of (you) to ...*
> ---
> The adjectives *nice / kind / sweet / generous* are often used in these patterns:
> It was very **kind of you to (give me a lift)**.
> It's very **nice of you to (help me move house)**.
> She paid for everything. It was **very generous of (her)**.

B Write the adjectives in brackets in the correct order to complete the text.

I think kids and teenagers today get quite a bad press. We're always hearing stories about how naughty or spoilt they are, but they can also be really [1] .... (wsete). I run an after-school club and on their first day, the kids are often very [2] .... (hys). When they get used to the routine, a lot of the younger kids are very [3] .... (oatetefafcin) to me and to each other. We are pretty strict and I think the kids respect that, even the ones whose parents are very [4] .... (ngtnuidle) and buy them everything they want. And many of these children are quite [5] .... (vctpoitemei) and ambitious for their future. Even some of the younger ones are [6] .... (dnemedtrei) to make something of themselves. OK, one or two of them can be a bit [7] .... (alyz) sometimes but that's true of a lot of adults, too.

C Which three adjectives would you use from exercises A and B about these people?

1 yourself ....
2 your best friend ....
3 your brother/sister/cousin ....
4 your favourite teacher ....

> **Learner tip**
> Try to link new vocabulary to yourself and to your own life as much as possible. This helps to make the vocabulary meaningful and helps you to remember it.

DEVELOPING CONVERSATIONS *That's like ...*

Draw a line to match the comments (1–5) and the responses (a–e).

1 My five-year-old won't speak to anyone she doesn't know.
2 My new neighbour is very nice but she never stops talking!
3 Kelly hasn't missed a training session since she decided to run the marathon.
4 Our new landlord seems very nice. He hasn't given us a list of rules and it's fine if the rent is a couple of days late.
5 When we go out, my friend Ali won't let me pay for anything.

a That's like my Uncle Joe. He's very generous too.
b That's like my little brother. He's very shy too.
c That's like my nephew, Luke. He's very determined too.
d That's like my manager. She's really easy-going too.
e That's like my old English teacher. He was really chatty too.

READING

A **Read the article quickly. Six parts have been removed. Write the correct letter (a–f) in the gaps in the article.**

a the eldest child often helps the younger ones with simple tasks.

b later research seems to suggest that birth order is in fact relevant

c there will be hundreds that don't.

d and the youngest has the reputation of being rebellious, creative, and sometimes spoilt.

e So, what might explain this difference?

f However, when a second child is born in the family,

B **Read the article again. Decide if these sentences are true or false.**

1 The writer thinks that ideas about birth order are just stereotypes.

2 Adler supported the idea that the youngest child is sometimes spoilt.

3 Norwegian scientists found that the cleverest child is often the oldest.

4 Being born first in a family can make you competitive.

5 Older children can benefit from teaching younger brothers and sisters.

6 The writer thinks that families should accept the ideas behind birth order.

C **Match the sentence halves.**

1 I adore my little brother but he's always the centre ......

2 I think I did well at school because my parents had ......

3 I did well in my career while my sister is a dropout, but it's impossible to come ......

4 I'm an only child but I don't think I fit ......

5 It's normal for children to be very different from each other even if parents bring ......

6 It's very hard for working parents to dedicate ......

a them up in more or less the same way.

b up with a reason why.

c a lot of time and energy to their children.

d high expectations of me.

e the stereotype of being spoilt.

f of attention when we have a family party.

Birth order
– myth or reality?

According to the theory of birth order, the child who is born first in a family tends to be hardworking, responsible and determined. The middle child is supposed to be competitive, outgoing and sociable, [1] … . But can your position in a family really have an effect, or are these ideas just silly stereotypes?

Scientists have been interested in this question for centuries and have given opinions both for and against the theory. Alfred Adler, an Austrian doctor working in the 1920s, believed that first-borns are special because at first they receive all the love and attention that the parents have to offer. [2] … they can often suffer feelings of rejection because they are no longer the centre of attention. Adler also thought that in families with three or more children, parents are more likely to be indulgent with the youngest.

Although Adler didn't come up with any scientific evidence for his ideas, [3] … . Scientists at the University of Oslo checked the results of intelligence tests from over 240 000 people. They found that first-borns are, on average, more intelligent than any siblings who follow later in the family. Other studies have shown that younger siblings tend to be shorter and lighter than first-borns, but it's the difference in intelligence that continues to interest scientists.

[4] … Psychologists suggest that the adults' role in bringing up a first-born child is as important as birth order. As there is no competition from other children, parents can dedicate a lot of time, money and resources (books, activities, classes, etc.) to the first-born child. When other children are born [5] … . The eldest child develops mental and social skills by being a tutor to his or her younger siblings. Parents also tend to be stricter with first-born children and have high expectations of them. This may explain why eldest children are often quite traditional but also very competent.

Of course, these ideas about birth order will never be completely accepted, because for every family that fits the stereotypes [6] … . But it can be interesting for parents to think about how they bring up their children and the differences between them as individuals.

Glossary

stereotypes: fixed ideas about a person or thing which are often not true
rejection: not showing someone the love or kindness they need
siblings: brother and sisters
resources: things that you can use to help you achieve something

GRAMMAR *Used to and would*

A Choose the correct forms.

When I [1] *was / used to be* a kid, I was a bit of a loner. I [2] *used to / would* love spending time by myself. I [3] *would / went* go to the beach and spend hours looking at the sea, or go for long walks. I [4] *played / used to play* with my friends at school, but I [5] *not used to / didn't* need to have company after school or at weekends. I think it's because I'm the third child of a family of five, so it [6] *used be / was* hard to get attention from my parents. They [7] *would / used* spend a lot of time with my eldest brother and my baby sister, so there wasn't much left for me. I [8] *wasn't / wouldn't be* sad about this – I knew my parents loved me – but it made me quite independent.

B Match the cues 1–6 and a–f. Write sentences with *used to* and then *would* or past simple. In one sentence, you can use only the past simple.

1 Amy / be very competitive ......
2 My dad / work shifts ......
3 Elisa / collect coins ......
4 I / be very close to my grandad ......
5 Adam / be quite spoilt ......
6 This area / be quite rough ......

a she / have about 500 from different countries
b he / leave the house while were all asleep
c we / spend hours together working in his garden
d he / get anything he asked for
e people / throw their litter all over the place
f she / spend hours preparing for tests

1 *Amy used to be very competitive. She would spend / spent hours preparing for tests.* ......
2 ....
....
3 ....
....
4 ....
....
5 ....
....
6 ....
....

VOCABULARY *Synonyms*

A Complete the spidergram with the words in the box. One word can go with two of the verbs.

a conversation	~~in power~~	in touch	in bed all day
a big challenge	a friendship	forgetting	a serious problem
~~together~~	something warm	a long-distance relationship	

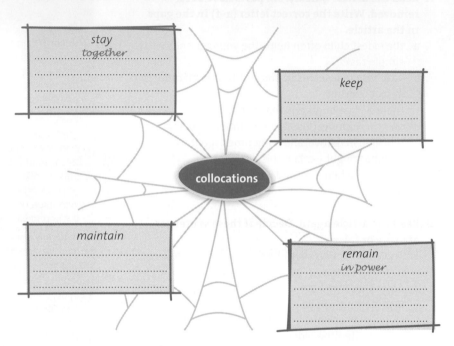

stay
together

keep

maintain

remain
in power

collocations

B Cross out any of the verbs that are not correct in these sentences. More than one may be wrong.

1 There's been an accident but please *keep / maintain / stay / remain* calm. There's an ambulance on its way.
2 Have you *stayed / kept / maintained / remained* friends with people from school?
3 My daughter *keeps / remains / stays / maintains* getting into trouble at school.
4 It's freezing out there, so try and *keep / remain / stay / maintain* warm by the open fire.
5 Don't forget to *keep / maintain / stay / remain* in touch while you're away travelling.
6 Put the wine in the fridge to *stay / remain / keep / maintain* it cold.
7 How do you try and *remain / stay / maintain / keep* fit?

C Choose the correct verbs and complete the sentences to make them true for you.

1 .... *remained / kept* in power in my country for many years.
2 I need to *keep / stay* trying to improve my ....
3 I've *maintained / stayed* contact with .... from my first school.
4 The economy *remains / maintains* strong in .... in my country.
5 I think it's important to *stay / maintain* quiet when other people ....
6 My country *maintains / remains* good relations with ....
7 I think I could *remain / maintain* in control if I ....

GRAMMAR Expressing regrets (*wish*)

A Put the verbs in the correct form to complete the sentences.

1 I got stuck in a traffic jam for hours. I wish I .... (go) by train.
2 My first boyfriend was really selfish and big-headed. I wish I .... (never / meet) him.
3 These shoes fell apart after two weeks. I wish I .... (never / buy) them.
4 The meal was tasty but a bit greasy. I wish .... (not / fry) the chicken.
5 I slipped and broke my leg on the first day. I wish I .... (never / try) skiing.
6 I like my open fire but it takes ages to warm up the room. I wish we .... (put in) central heating.
7 I have an enormous workload and tight deadlines. I wish I .... (choose) a different course.
8 We left the film halfway through because my son was scared. I wish they .... (warn) me about the special effects.

B Write sentences with I *wish* and the verbs in the box. Then match the sentences to the list of regrets (a–f).

> not fall out with my dad   spend time with my kids   visit Brazil   not be late for my son's graduation
> marry the love of my life   not leave my degree course

1 ....
We haven't spoken to each
other for years.

2 ....
My parents were born there
but I've never been.

3 .... I've
never met anyone like her since

4 ....
It was the proudest moment
of his life.

5 .... I'm
stuck in a low-paid job now.

6 .... I was
always working and I left my
wife to bring them up.

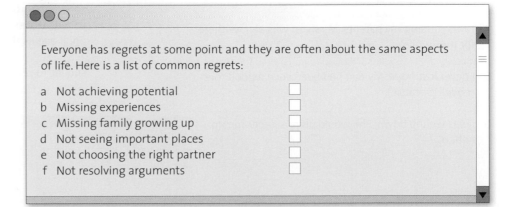

Everyone has regrets at some point and they are often about the same aspects of life. Here is a list of common regrets:

a Not achieving potential ☐
b Missing experiences ☐
c Missing family growing up ☐
d Not seeing important places ☐
e Not choosing the right partner ☐
f Not resolving arguments ☐

DEVELOPING WRITING
A profile – describing a person

A Complete the description with the words in the box.

as	Although	so that	despite
when	Because of	While	

B Join the pairs of sentences with the words in brackets.

The person who influenced me most is my maths teacher, Mike Kingsley. I used to be painfully shy and I would sit at the back of the class, hiding behind all the other kids. [1] .... *I was quite bright, I would never put my hand up to answer the questions. Then I started in Mr Kingsley's class* [2] .... *I was 11. He made the lessons fun* [3] .... *he would explain complicated ideas with stories or everyday objects.* [4] .... *his teaching style, my confidence grew and I became better and better at maths.* [5] .... *I was preparing for my A-level exams, Mike pushed me to do my best. He gave me confidence in my ability* [6] .... *I was able to take the exams a year early. I went on to do a degree in maths, and,* [7] .... *living a long way away, we stayed in touch. He encouraged me to do a teacher-training course and now I have my dream job - teaching maths to young people.*

1 I was quite naughty at school. My parents still believed in me. (although)

....

2 My coach made me a determined person. I became a professional footballer. (so that)

....

3 I had a lot of problems. My friends always supported me. (despite)

....

4 I was missing my parents. My sister was always there for me. (while)

....

5 I never lost hope. My dad had been such a good role model. (because)

....

6 I was feeling down. She would always cheer me up. (when)

....

> **Learner tip**
>
> Try to link your ideas together when you write, using connecting words like those in exercises A and B. Some words and expressions have similar meaning but are used in different ways, e.g. *but, however, despite, in spite of*. Keep a note of these differences in your vocabulary notebook.

C An online magazine has launched a competition with the title: *A person who has influenced my life*. Write a description of the person and how he / she has influenced you. (120–150 words).

LISTENING

A 🔊 12.1 Read the notes through quickly. Then listen to Part 1 and complete the information.

http//www.friendshipischanging.com

IS FRIENDSHIP CHANGING IN THE 21ST CENTURY?

According to research from the early .... , people have an average of .... contacts in their social network. This includes about .... close friends. But thanks to the .... , some people claim to have hundreds or even .... of friends on social networking sites like 'Facebook' and MySpace. These friends may even include .... people who join the sites. However, a recent survey how shown that the actual number of true online friends is just .... So, it seems that maintaining .... in cyberspace is similar to real life.

B 🔊 **12.2 You are going to hear four people talking about their friends. Listen to Part 2. Are these statements true or false?**

1 Natalie thinks Internet friendships are as real as traditional friendships.
2 Her only friends are on the Internet.
3 William has contact with a lot of people he doesn't know well.
4 He has only a couple of close friends.
5 Adrian says he feels lonely.
6 He isn't interested in Internet friendships.
7 Trisha hasn't kept in touch with her schoolfriends.
8 She doesn't get on well with the people on her course.

PRONUNCIATION
Connected speech

A Mark the links in the sentences from Listening.

1 I have hundreds of friends all over the world

2 I have friends at college that I meet up with every day

3 I have a lot of colleagues and a big circle of acquaintances

4 We keep in touch as much as possible

5 Well, I'm a bit of a loner

6 My circle of friends is quite small

7 I'm quite outgoing and chatty

8 I've also made a lot of new friends on my course

B 🔊 **12.3 Listen and check. Then practise saying the sentences.**

Vocabulary Builder Quiz 12 (*OVB* pp46–48)

Try the *OVB* quiz for Unit 12. Write your answers in your notebook. Then check them and record your score.

A Which words are missing from the hyphenated examples?
1 After 20 years of friendship, they had a big falling-..............
2 My ....-grandparents were born in Poland.
3 There was a huge queue at all the ....-in desks.
4 This camera was £300. It was such a rip-..............
5 My mum divorced my dad and married again so I have two .... -brothers.
6 My new boss seems pretty ....-going.

B Match the sentence halves.

1 I don't think it		a a phase of being very naughty.
2 It was such a nice surprise to come		b getting into working as a volunteer?
3 Before I start college, I think I might go		c will do you any harm to stay up late for once.
4 My two year old son is going through		d backpacking around Europe.
5 When did you start		e character for her to start crying.
6 It seemed very out of		f across a pile of old love letters.

C Which preposition can complete the sentences in each pair?
1 We were stuck on the side of the road for ages after we broke ....
Let's stay in for a while. I think it's going to pour ....
2 I don't know why she walked .... on her entire family.
Did you know he's dropping .... of his degree course.
3 Why are they getting married? They don't have very much .... common.
What's the best way to get back .... touch with old school friends?

D Which adjectives from OVB 12 can complete the sentences?
1 Amy used to be shy but she's getting more .... now.
2 I've never known such an .... child. She's always hugging and kissing everyone.
3 My aunt gave me some money when I graduated. It was really .... of her.
4 He should lighten up. He's so .... about everything.
5 They give those kids everything they want. I think it's a mistake to be so ....

E What form of the words in brackets do you need to complete the text?
They are threatening to close down our local hospital. Local people think it's an [1] (idiot) idea and are [2] (determination) to keep it open. I went on a [3] (demonstrate) last week against the plan. It was a really [4] (power) experience to see so many people united with the same aim. Our main problem will be dealing with the director of the hospital, who is so [5] (ego) that he never listens to anyone. I hope that we can get him to see sense.

Score ____ /25

**Wait a couple of weeks and try the quiz again.
Compare your scores.**

13 TRAVEL

VOCABULARY
Ways of travelling and travel problems

A Choose the correct words.

1 We couldn't afford a summer holiday, so we went on a few *day* / *days* trips instead.

2 I'm useless at travelling *slim* / *light*. I always end up with at least three bags.

3 I'd love to go to Australia but it's such a long *travel* / *journey* from home.

4 The first time I went abroad was on a *business* / *school* trip with my classmates.

5 We're taking a gap year and going *travelling* / *traveller* before university.

6 If I go on a *shopping* / *hunting* trip, I never find any bargains.

B Complete the conversations with the words in the boxes.

carriage	platform	line

1 A: How come you're so late?
   B: A guy at the station sent to me to the wrong ....
      and then there was a tree blocking the .... after last night's storm.
   A: Did you manage to get a seat?
   B: You're joking! The .... was absolutely packed.

deck	harbour	crossing

2 A: I'm never going by ferry ever again!
   B: Why? What happened?
   A: The .... was really rough. I spent the whole time up on the .... trying not to be sick.
   B: Oh, dear, but at least you got a good view of the ....

bend	tyre	traffic lights

3 A: Be careful here. There are some .... about halfway down here so you might have to stop. And then there's a very tight .... in the road.
   B: OK, thanks.
   A: And it looks like there's some broken glass along here. Let's turn off – you don't want to end up with a flat ....
   B: OK, I'll take a left here.

security	check-in desk	take-off

4 A: How was your flight?
   B: Well, ... and landing were fine, but the start of the journey wasn't great.
   A: How come?
   B: They had only one .... open, so it took ages. Then I kept setting the alarm off when I went through .... It was so embarrassing.

C Find six adjectives in the word snake. Match them with words they often describe.

wrongstupidterrifyingbumpyhugeslippery

1 .... question / mistake / idea
2 .... road / flight / track
3 .... waves / queue / crowd
4 .... road / pavement / floor
5 .... turning / platform / direction
6 .... experience / journey / sound

LISTENING

A 🔊 13.1 Listen to the first part of a radio programme on commuting – travelling to and from work every day. What type of programme is it?

a a business programme
b a lifestyle programme
c a news programme

B 🔊 **13.2 Listen to the complete programme. Choose the correct answer to the questions, a, b, or c.**

1 How long do most people in the UK spend commuting a day?
   a 19 minutes
   b an hour
   c three quarters of an hour
2 To avoid very packed trains, Penny suggests
   a adapting your timetable.
   b trying a different carriage.
   c changing your form of transport.
3 Which activity does Penny think train commuters should avoid?
   a reading
   b working
   c knitting
4 People who have to stand on a train can benefit from
   a having positive thoughts.
   b talking to other commuters.
   c finding a personal space.
5 What can put commuters in a bad mood?
   a having no one to talk to
   b feeling tired
   c listening to other people's complaints
6 You can reduce stress levels by
   a commuting by car.
   b trying some gentle physical exercise.
   c doing aerobics after work.

Language note sounds that aren't pronounced

In some longer words, we don't always pronounce all the syllables, e.g.
chocolate   /ˈtʃɒklət/ two syllables, not three
vegetables   /ˈvedʒtəblz/ three syllables, not four

PRONUNCIATION
Sounds that aren't pronounced

A Cross out the letters that aren't pronounced in the **underlined** words.

1 *Lifestyles,* the programme that tries to make life just a bit more manageable.
2 Penny Marshall, professional life coach in the business sector.
3 People in the UK spend an average of 45 minutes travelling to and from work.
4 People use different forms of transport to get to work.
5 Let's start with travellers by train.

B Now cross out the letters that aren't pronounced in these extracts.

1 you get a seat in a quieter carriage
2 preferably something you enjoy rather than work
3 several of my clients take knitting on the train
4 that can be very uncomfortable
5 more interesting advice for commuters

C 🔊 **13.3 Listen and check. Then practise saying the examples.**

VOCABULARY Phrasal verbs

Complete the story with a verb from box A and a particle from box B.

A	calm	set	check	hanging	worked	go
	pour	got				

B	in	down	around	through	back	off
	down	out				

I really can't stand [1] ....
airports. I always [2] .... far too
early and then I have loads of time to kill. It's so dull
sitting around and drinking endless cups of coffee.
So, instead of flying on my latest business trip, I
decided to drive. I [3] .... my
route on my sat nav, packed all the stuff I needed, and
[4] .... nice and early. I was just
enjoying the scenery, when suddenly the weather
changed. The clouds were so thick that I lost the signal
on the sat nav. Then it started to
[5] .... The rain was so heavy I
couldn't see the road in front of me. I needed to be at
the ferry by 10:30, so I decided to keep going, despite
the weather. A few minutes later, the car started to
feel bumpy and I realised I had a flat tyre. I couldn't
believe it. I was so annoyed and frustrated but I knew
I had to [6] .... and just change
the wheel. By the time I [7] ....
into the car, I was completely soaked and very fed up.
I arrived at the harbour just in time to see the ferry
starting its crossing. What a nightmare! I never want to
[8] .... a journey like that again.

13

GRAMMAR Third conditionals

A Choose the correct forms.

1 If I'd / would listened to the news, I'd have known that the motorway was closed.
2 I don't know what we would have done if our visas wouldn't / hadn't arrived in time.
3 If the ferry crossing hadn't been so rough, we can / could have had a nice meal.
4 Would you have stayed in England if you didn't / hadn't married a Brazilian woman?
5 The police would / wouldn't have stopped you if you hadn't been speeding.
6 If they hadn't escaped from their own country, they might have / had been arrested.

B Read the conversations. There is one word missing in each of B's lines. Add the word in the correct place.

1 A: Poor Mike. He missed his plane because he ended up at the wrong terminal.
   B: If he'd checked the details before, he would caught his plane.
2 A: Whatever happened to Joanne? Wasn't she your best friend from college?
   B: If she hadn't emigrated to Canada, we might have in touch.
3 A: Why on earth didn't you ring me about the train delay?
   B: If I been able to get a signal on my mobile, I would have let you know.
4 A: That taxi from the airport cost us a fortune.
   B: We could have caught the bus to the hotel if you hung around for so long.
5 A: What made you want to emigrate to Australia?
   B: To be honest, we'd have stayed in the UK if there hadn't so much unemployment.
6 A: How come you let them confiscate your laptop?
   B: If I hadn't agreed, they wouldn't allowed me on the plane.

READING

A Why might places in the world become impossible to visit? Match the four places in the article with the reasons a–d.

People stopped visiting / using:

1 Bikini Atoll, an island in the Pacific Ocean
2 Mount Elgon, Kenya
3 The Panama Railway
4 Gorongosa National Park, Mozambique

because

a the line was in very bad condition.
b of a civil war.
c of nuclear testing.
d it is situated on the border between two countries who were arguing about land.

B Read the article quickly and check your answers to exercise A.

C Read the article again. Write the correct places. Which place ...

1 has had financial help from different people?
....
2 can be reached by car?
....
3 doesn't appear to have suffered from its history?
....
4 took five years to construct?
....
5 doesn't have any people living there?
....
6 can be explored from the inside?
....
7 combines a journey with observing wildlife?
....
8 used to be a big tourist attraction?
....

D What do these numbers in the article refer to?

1958 (line 2)
45 (line 19)
470km (line 31)
200m (line 37)
12 000 (line 42)
1 862m (line 51)

E Replace the underlined words in the sentences with the words in bold in the article.

1 To walk a long distance over hills or mountains isn't my idea of a perfect holiday.
2 It was a beautiful harbour until they transformed it into a tourist destination.
3 Tourism has really taken off since difficult relationships have improved between the two countries.
4 The region attracts a lot of people who like walking in the countryside.
5 The most amazing aspect of the journey were the amazing views from the ship.
6 The island was supposed to be an unchanged paradise but it was more like a concrete jungle.

LOST DESTINATIONS NOW BACK ON THE LIST

Global travel is getting easier and more popular, giving the impression that you can go where you want, when you want. However, environmental changes and human influences mean that travel destinations are always changing. Here are a few places that you couldn't have gone to 10 years ago.

Bikini Atoll, Micronesia

This was the main area of nuclear testing in the Pacific. There were 23 tests on this small island from 1946 to 1958. When you have flown in from Honolulu, you might be surprised at what you find. Despite its nuclear past, the area looks like an **unspoilt** tropical paradise. The island
5 itself is still uninhabited, but a 1998 report said that Bikini is now safe to live on. Thanks to a recent rise in tourism, popular activities include diving and fishing off the beautiful coastline.

Mount Elgon, Kenya

For years, border disputes between Kenya and Uganda
25 meant it was impossible to **trek** over this extinct volcano. Now **tensions have eased**, so this far corner of east Africa has reopened. The mountain and
30 the national park around it are well worth the 470km drive from Nairobi. Climbers can enjoy the incredible view from the top of Mount Elgon (4321m) but
35 perhaps the most fascinating **feature** is the caves. Some are over 60m wide and run 200m into the mountain. They are home to wild elephants that dig
40 for salts in the walls of the caves.

The Panama Railway

The world's first transcontinental railway was built between 1850 and
10 1855. It not only connected two cities – Panama City and the port of Colon – but also two oceans – the Pacific and the Atlantic. The line had been in disrepair for many years
15 until areas of land were cleared and new track was laid over a period of 18 months. In July 2001 it was reopened, offering a 45-minute ride though a
20 jungle area with spider monkeys and caimans.

Gorongosa National Park, Mozambique

In 1971, this magnificent wildlife park attracted 12 000 visitors who wanted to see the biggest lion population in Africa. From 1983–1992 the park was **turned**
45 into an environmental disaster area during Mozambique's civil war. After the war, the number of large animals in the park had fallen by 95%. Now, buffalo have been reintroduced and the park has received
50 donations from businesspeople and pop stars. You won't find cheetahs or rhinos back in the park yet, but the beautiful Mount Gorongosa (1 862m) is perfect for **hikers**.

Glossary

atoll: a coral island in the shape of a ring
caiman: a reptile related to the alligator

13

VOCABULARY Strong adjectives

A Choose the correct adjective from each group to complete the sentences.

1 Jenny makes absolutely.....................cakes. (tasty / delicious / nice)
2 You don't want to go to Egypt in the summer. It's absolutely........................ . (boiling / hot / warm)
3 No wonder she won the literature prize. Her first novel is absolutely .... (interesting / good / fascinating)
4 When I told her I had crashed the car she was absolutely .... (annoyed / furious / angry)
5 I'm enjoying my new job but I have an absolutely .... workload. (huge / large / big)
6 When will lunch be ready? I'm absolutely .... (hungry / starving / overeating)

B Complete the conversations with the phrases in the box.

absolutely freezing	really fantastic
absolutely exhausting	absolutely packed
completely soaked	really filthy

1 A: Mum said the film was good.
   B: Yeah, the special effects were ....
2 A: Did you end up getting wet in all that rain?
   B: I didn't have a jacket, so I got ....
3 A: Your daily commute is over an hour, isn't it? I bet that's tiring.
   B: It's .... but it's only for a few months more.
4 A: The water around the coast is supposed to be quite dirty.
   B: I wouldn't swim in it – it looked .... to me.
5 A: Jan was telling me that the hotel was quite crowded.
   B: You can say that again. It was ....
6 A: I bet it was cold in New York over Christmas.
   B: It was ....I couldn't feel my feet during the whole trip.

GRAMMAR Should have

Write a response for each sentence with should / shouldn't have and the verbs in the box.

set off earlier	not wear high-heels	not make so much noise
apply for it earlier	ask for an extension	not pack so much stuff
not stay up so late	ask someone for directions	

1 We missed our ferry to France. We *should've set off earlier* .
2 My feet were killing me by the time we got back to the hotel. You ....
3 Jack's visa didn't arrive in time for his trip. He ....
4 I hurt my back while lifting my suitcase. I ....
5 I feel completely exhausted this morning. You ....
6 Allie missed the deadline for her essay. She ....
7 We ended up in the middle of the old town, completely lost. You ....
8 The neighbours complained about our party on Saturday. We ....

DEVELOPING CONVERSATIONS
Blaming people

Choose the correct words.

1 A: Look at this phone bill. It's huge.
   B: Don't blame [1] *me / myself*. It's not my [2] *blame / fault*. I hardly ever use the phone.
   A: It must be the [3] *kids / kids'* fault, then. We should have [4] *told / tell* them to ask before they make a call.
2 A: Vicky didn't do too well in her exams. I [5] *fault / blame* myself. I [6] *must've / should've* given her more help with her revision.
   B: It's not your fault – it's [7] *herself / hers*. She's bright. If [8] *she'd / she would* worked harder, she would have passed easily.
3 A: If you ask me, it's the guide's [9] *blame / fault*. He [10] *should've / should of* checked the area before they set off.
   B: It's [11] *nobody / nobody's* fault. It was an accident. It could have [12] *happen / happened* to anyone.

DEVELOPING WRITING
A description – using interesting language

A Read the description quickly. Circle the parts where the writer describes what she could:
- see
- smell
- hear

Language note describing senses

We often use *could + see / smell / hear / taste / feel* to describe senses in the past.
I **could see** the waves crashing against the harbour wall.

Vocabulary Builder Quiz 13 (*OVB* pp50–52)

Try the *OVB* quiz for Unit 13. Write your answers in your notebook. Then check them and record your score.

A Which is the odd one out in each set?

1 line	bend	traffic lights	tyre
2 crossing	fence	harbour	deck
3 check-in	landing	take-off	security
4 immigration	visa	passport	bump

B Complete the adjectives that begin with . . . *less*.

1 This photocopier is completely ....less. It's always breaking down.
2 I thought the vase was quite valuable but unfortunately it turned out to be ....less.
3 Check your work to make sure you haven't made any ....less mistakes.
4 I was a bit scared of the dentist but the treatment was ....less.
5 I'm exhausted. I've had so many ....less nights.
6 When they told me I'd won first prize, I was ....less.

C Which words are missing from the verbs?

1 What time shall I pick you .... at the station?
2 I'd like to set .... a book club at my school.
3 We need to work .... the quickest way to the airport.
4 We need to make up .... the loss of profit last year.
5 Why are you so angry? I think you need to calm .... a bit.
6 Which towns did you go .... on the way here?

D Complete the sentences with words that begin with *re ... .*

1 Can I borrow your mobile? I forgot to re............ mine.
2 I'm sorry but those seats are already re............
3 There are lots of re............ about what you can put in your hand luggage.
4 I've got a re............ for a double room in the name of Marshall.
5 The doctor told him to re............ the amount of alcohol he drinks.
6 They're busy at weekends, so it's a good idea to re............ a table.

E Which word do you need to complete the sentences in each set?

1 What's the number of the help .... ?
There's no-one at the information ....
Please leave the keys at the reception ....
2 I always pack too much. I need to learn to .... light.
Do you .... much for work?
It's my ambition to .... the world.
3 .... is very tight at the airport after the bomb scare.
I always get stopped when I go through ....
There are always .... guards outside the prime minister's house.

Score ___/25

Wait a couple of weeks and try the quiz again.
Compare your scores.

● ● ○

OG BLOG BLOG BLOG BLOG BLOG BLOG BLOG BLOG
OG BLOG BLOG BLOG BLOG BLOG BLOG BLOG BLOG
OG BLOG BLOG BLOG BLOG BLOG BLOG BLOG BLOG
OG BLOG BLOG BLOG BLOG BLOG TRAVELBLOG BLOG
OG BLOG BLOG BLOG BLOG BLOG BLOG BLOG BLOG

Our journey started on ¹ an empty railway platform. The temperature had dropped to minus 3° the night before and it was still ² very cold. I was ³ very tired after a ⁴ bad night's sleep and I wasn't looking forward to the trip. The station was ⁵ very quiet until the train arrived a few minutes later. The sun started to rise as we set off and I could see ⁶ nice stripes of red and orange across the sky. Suddenly, I could smell hot coffee. We had skipped breakfast and I realised I was ⁷ very hungry. At that moment a man appeared selling coffee and ⁸ big pieces of sweet bread – it was ⁹ very nice. After a few stops along the line, we could hear people talking and laughing. Moments later, our carriage was ¹⁰ full of local people going to market. They wore traditional clothes in ¹¹ nice colours and they were very friendly. They told us ¹² interesting stories and gave us advice about the next part of our trip. By the time we reached our stop, we had made lots of ¹³ nice new friends.

B Replace the underlined adjectives with more descriptive words.

1 an empty   *a deserted*

Learner tip

Using descriptive language when you write is a good way of keeping your reader interested. This is also true in speaking, when you talk about what has happened to you, or tell a story.

C Write a description of a journey (120–150 words). It can be a positive or a negative experience. Try to include the following:

• descriptions of what you could see / smell / hear / taste / feel
• interesting language including strong adjectives
• -ing clauses (see SB p77)

VOCABULARY Computers

A Choose the correct words.

1 Using a *scanner / printer* is a quick way of getting photos in digital format.
2 If something on your computer doesn't work, check everything is plugged in to the correct *socket / cursor*.
3 It's best to get a computer with an external *keyboard / hard drive* so that you can keep all your work safe.
4 I wish I'd bought a laptop with a bigger *screen / mouse* – it's hard to use when I have a lot of documents open.
5 If you want to download a very big *menu / file*, it can take quite a long time.
6 You'll need an extension lead if the *plug / cable* is too short to reach the wall.

B Complete the conversations using the words that weren't the answers in exercise A.

1 A How do I check the number of words in my essay?
  B If you go to the Tools ...., you'll find the word count feature there.
2 A I've never used a computer before. What's that arrow on the screen?
  B That's called the .... You use it to select the point on the screen where you want to do something.
3 A What on earth is the matter with that .... ?
  B It's probably just run out of paper. No one ever replaces it in this office.
4 A Kelly, don't use the .... right on top of the desk. You might damage it. You need to use the little mat we gave you.
  B OK, Dad, sorry.
5 A I'll need to use this laptop in the USA and South America. Will the .... be OK?
  B Don't worry, sir, you get a free international adapter to fit all two- and three-pin systems.
6 A I get real backache every time I use the computer.
  B I think your hands are too far from the .... It means you have to stretch every time you type.

C Match the sentence halves.

1 I was about to print out my essay when the screen ......
2 I don't know what was going on. I tried clicking on ......
3 I had just updated my CV, but I deleted ......
4 No wonder her computer wouldn't work. She'd spilt ......
5 Since I lost a 3 000-word essay, I always make ......
6 I spent ages checking the printer before I realised it wasn't plugged ......
7 If you want to send the photos by email, you'll need to scan ......
8 If you click on the different icons, it will ......
9 This office is such a mess. Be careful you don't trip ......

a display drop-down menus of different options.
b the images first.
c back-up copies of all my work.
d water all over the keyboard.
e the file by mistake and had to start all over again.
f over the cable from the printer to the wall.
g in to the correct socket.
h the icon but the document wouldn't open.
i froze and I had to restart my laptop.

DEVELOPING CONVERSATIONS
Responding to advice

Choose the correct words.

1 A: Oh, hell. Why won't this microphone *work / to work*?
  B: Have you checked the *connected / connection*?
  A: No, I haven't.
  B: Well, try that. *In that case / Otherwise*, you might have to ask IT for a new *one / other*.
2 A: I don't believe it! I've just lost a huge *file / icon*.
  B: Have you *made / done* a search for it?
  A: Yeah, but it didn't *work / success*.
3 A: Oh, no! My computer's *broken / crashed* again.
  B: Have you tried *freezing / rebooting* it at all?
  A: No, not *still / yet*.
  B: Well, try that. Otherwise, I don't know what *else / other* you can do.
4 A: No, please don't *start / stop* working now! I have to print this essay.
  B: Have you checked the printer cartridge at all?
  A: Yeah, but it made no *difference / success*.
  B: Sorry, I can't really help. You're *have / best* taking it to a shop.

DEVELOPING WRITING

An essay – discussing pros and cons

A Read the essay quickly. Choose the correct answer, a, b or c.

The writer thinks:

a using computers is the best way to learn.

b you need a balance of different input in education.

c students shouldn't be allowed to use the Internet.

> **Learner tip**
>
> Each paragraph in an essay needs a topic sentence. This is usually the first sentence and it tells the reader what the paragraph is about. The following sentences give more details and/or examples of the topic.

B The writer should have divided the essay into four separate paragraphs. Read it again and mark where each new paragraph should start.

The use of computers in education has increased enormously over the last decade. Students of all ages make use of computer technology both inside the classroom and at home. Some students even take their exams online. So what are the pros and cons of this revolution in education? There are obviously several benefits to using computers. Firstly, they allow students to work more quickly and easily than in the past. Secondly, they can work independently from their teacher and at their own pace. Thirdly, they can review and change their work until they have got it right. On the other hand, there are also problems with computers. Some students depend very heavily on the Internet, which can lead to a fall in creativity. It is difficult for students to select information from the Net due to the huge number of websites. If students have only computer-based lessons, they can become rather isolated. In conclusion, I think there is an important role for computers in education, but students also need other learning opportunities. This can include working in groups, taking part in project work, doing experiments and going on trips.

C Underline the topic sentence in each paragraph of the essay.

D What is the main function of each paragraph in the essay? Choose a or b.

1 a to describe the current situation
   b to give the writer's overall opinion

2 a to say how the writer benefits from computers
   b to describe the advantages of computers

3 a to describe the disadvantages of computers
   b to criticise technology companies

4 a to give the writer's overall opinion
   b to describe the future of computers

E Write an essay (150–180 words) based on the title below. Remember to:

- think about the pros and cons of using technology, and make notes
- write a topic sentence for each paragraph, then give more details and/or examples
- use connecting words and phrases to link sentences and paragraphs.
- check your essay carefully when you have finished

'People today depend too much on technology in everyday life.'
How far do you agree with this statement?

VOCABULARY Talking about markets

A Match the follow-up comments in the box to the sentences 1–7.

> a The property business is booming.
> b The gold and silver markets are in decline.
> c The hotel market is still growing.
> d The cigarette market has been fairly steady for a while.
> e The market for fossil fuels is completely dead.
> f Agriculture is big business right now.
> g The cosmetics market is completely saturated.

1 You don't want to set up a make-up range. ......
2 If you want a hot tip, get into construction. ......
3 I'm afraid you've missed your opportunity to make money out of metals. ......
4 If you hurry, you could make money out of tourism. ......
5 You won't make an instant profit on tobacco but then you won't lose either. ......
6 Don't miss out on investing in wheat and rice. ......
7 It's just not worth putting money into oil. ......

B Replace the <u>underlined</u> words in the sentences with the words and expressions in the box. There are two expressions that you don't need.

> is bigger than it used to be
> growing steadily
> almost saturated
> tiny
> huge
> is smaller than it used to be
> is bigger than it was 20 years ago
> is smaller than it was 20 years ago

1 The market for sports cars <u>has risen in the last 20 years</u>.
2 Interest in the foreign property market <u>has gone down</u>.
3 Don't go into shoe or handbag design. The market for accessories is <u>nearly full of products</u>.
4 The market for expensive jewellery is <u>very small</u> in the 17–25 age range.
5 Due to increases in immigration, the market for specialist food is <u>increasing in a gradual and regular way</u>.
6 The demand for antique gold and silver items used to be <u>very big</u>, but it has declined in recent years.

READING

A Read the article quickly and choose the most appropriate heading.

a Museum works with the Internet to find stolen art
b The wonder of the art world at the click of a mouse
c Art on the Internet will replace real paintings

B Read the article again. Choose the correct answers.

1 People can see some of the Prado's most famous paintings from their computer after Google
   a created a special new program.
   b wanted art lovers to have a virtual tour of the museum.
   c found a new use for existing technology.
2 If you view the paintings online, you can
   a see paintings that have never been seen before.
   b see how the painter constructed the images.
   c see only sections of the images.
3 What does paragraph 3 say about the paintings?
   a They are by a range of artists but you are not allowed to get close to them.
   b They are by a range of artists but they are too big for the gallery.
   c They are by a range of artists and some of them are huge.
4 The paintings reproduced by Google are clear because
   a of the quality of the digital photography.
   b Google took 14 000 photographs.
   c they had been restored earlier.
5 What is Miguel Zugaza referring to when he says the word *here* (line 66)?
   a in the photographs of the paintings
   b in the Prado
   c in global art museums
6 Why does Miguel Zugaza think the original paintings can't be replaced by photographs?
   a more people will see the originals
   b the originals are more moving
   c the originals are in a global art museum

C Choose the correct words.

1 Some TV companies have *changed / moved* into computers and now supply Internet connections.
2 The computer won't allow you *accessible / access* to the files without the correct password.
3 It was great. We took a *virtual / technical* tour of the museum before we got there so that we knew which galleries we wanted to see for real.
4 I used to be rubbish at taking photos, but now I can improve them *automatically / digitally* on my computer, they don't look too bad.
5 Looking at the image under a microscope showed details that were invisible to the *naked / open* eye.
6 I don't take part in sport very often – I'm more of *an armchair / a sofa* sportsman.

Google Earth, the virtual globe and map program that allows armchair tourists to see the world, has moved into the world of art. One

5 of the most famous galleries in the world – the Prado in Madrid – has allowed Google access to 14 of its masterpieces. Using the same technology that builds a photographic

10 map of the world, art lovers can now view paintings by some of the world's most famous artists online.

The technology gives Internet users the opportunity to move their cursor

15 across the surface of the paintings and click on details that would be invisible to the naked eye, including individual brush strokes. "It allows people to see the main masterworks

20 in the museum as they have never done before," the museum said. "You can see details that the human eye alone is unable to see."

Las Meninas, the famous portrait

25 by Diego Velazquez of the family of Philip IV of Spain, is one of the paintings that can be viewed online. Other works include Francisco de Goya's El Tres de Mayo, Peter Paul

30 Rubens's The Three Graces and paintings by Titian, El Greco and Rembrandt. Some of the originals are so large that it is impossible to get close enough to see the tiny details.

35 "You would need a three-metre-high stepladder," said Clara Rivera of Google.

Google took thousands of high-resolution photographs of sections

40 of the paintings. The images had a resolution of 14000 megapixels – 1400 times higher than a picture taken on a standard 10 megapixel camera. The photographs were then

45 joined together digitally to reproduce all the details of the original canvas. The director of the Prado, Miguel Zugaza, said that he had used the Google images to check the quality

50 of restoration work done earlier on some of the paintings. "What this project offers is a level of definition that normally only we, the staff of the museum, see," he also said.

55 The Prado and Google have shown that technology can make art located in Madrid accessible to millions of people all over the world. Miguel Zugaza said he thought

60 the experiment could become the beginning of a global art museum. However, he also said that a photograph could never replace the original. "This shows you the body

65 of the painting, but what you won't find here is the soul. You can only find that by looking at the original."

Glossary

masterpiece: the best work of art an artist/musician/writer, etc. has ever produced
brush stroke: a mark left on a surface by a brush
resolution: the amount of detail you can see on a screen or in a photo
soul: the aspect of art, music, etc. that affects people's emotions

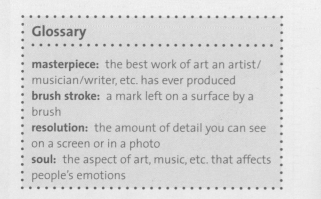

VOCABULARY
Technology, programs and gadgets

A Choose the correct words.

1 A: This PC is so slow. We need to *upload / upgrade* to something more *powerful / fast*.

B: How about one of those netbooks? They're a really nice *design / icon*. They look really *well / cool*.

A: You can't buy a computer because it's pretty!

B: I know but a netbook would be *heavier / lighter* and easier to *carry / wear* than my old laptop.

2 A: I can't believe how technology has changed. We've just bought an external hard drive with *100GB / 100GPS* so we can *keep / store* my work files and all our games and films.

B: I know what you mean. I came across a gadget that *lets / allows* you to transform cassettes into different *programs / formats*.

A: That sounds cool.

B: But one thing that worries me is my kids and the Internet – there is a lot of adult material.

A: Most computers have a program that *warnings / warns* you when you're about to visit *a dangerous / an endangered* website.

B Choose two of the three words to complete the sentences.

●○○

| What's your dream gadget / piece of technology? | Search | reply |

Posted by Wolf (3) ★ New member

A huge TV! My old one is rubbish. I'd like one with a bigger .... so that the .... is a lot clearer. (picture / format / screen)

Posted by Becks (4128) ★ ★ ★ Senior member

Central heating. We have open fires, so our little house is freezing most of the time. I'd love to be able to .... the timer and let the heating .... itself on.
(plug / switch / set)

Posted by Stu (19) ★ New member

An oven that cooks the dinner! I could .... such a lot of time because it would do it all ....
(digitally / save / automatically)

Posted by Josh (-) ★ ★ ★ ★ ★ Administrator

An environmentally-friendly car! It would .... off solar panels so it would be a lot ....
(go / greener / run)

Posted by Louise88 (107) ★ ★ Member

They already exist – low-energy light bulbs! I have them in every room in my flat. They .... on electricity bills because they're more energy ....
(efficient / safe / save)

Posted by Warrior (596) ★ ★ ★ Regular

A sat nav! I'm hoping to get one for my birthday. They're just so easy to .... and they make getting around really .... (straightforward / use / useful)

GRAMMAR
-ing forms and to-infinitives

Complete the questions with the correct form of the verbs in brackets. Then give true answers.

TECHNOLOGY — A TREAT OR A TRAUMA?

1 If you have a problem with your computer, how long do you keep .... (try) to solve it?

2 What makes you decide .... (get) a new gadget / update?

3 In what situations do you need to ask for help .... (sort out) a technical problem?

4 How often have you been guilty of .... (buy) a gadget that you don't really need?

5 How long does it take you to get used to .... (use) a new computer program / .... (drive) a different car?

6 What do you think about children .... (have) computer-based lessons in school?

7 Which gadget do you look forward to .... (use) most each day?

8 How easy is it for you .... (accept) changes in technology?

9 How long did it take you to learn .... (send) your first email?

10 Have you ever threatened to .... (throw away) a piece of technology that failed .... (work)?

LISTENING

A 🔊 **14.1 You are going to hear three short recordings about a man called Richard. Read the list of what happened to him. Then listen to Parts 1–3 and number the events in order.**

a He started his presentation in quite a confident way. ......

b He was delayed by heavy traffic. ......

c He didn't realise he was talking to the managing director. ......

d He realised he had loaded the wrong disk into his laptop. ......

e He had a problem with some equipment for his presentation. ......

f He programmed his sat nav and set off. ......

B Listen again. Are these statements true or false?

1 Richard set off late for his interview.

2 The sat nav tried to send the car down a road where it shouldn't go.

3 Richard was 40 minutes late.

4 The receptionist was expecting Richard.

5 Richard needed a replacement microphone.

6 The managing director helped Richard set up his equipment.

7 The interviewers couldn't see the screen very well during the presentation.

8 Richard has picked up his daughter's disk of photos.

9 The interviewers invited him to come back another time.

PRONUNCIATION Same sound or different?

A Are the letters in bold the same sound (S) or different (D)?

1 Yes, you're in r**oo**m 211. / That's very g**oo**d of you. ......

2 I've got everything I need for my pr**e**sentation. / The market for organic food has risen st**ea**dily. ......

3 At the end of the road, t**u**rn right. / Take the th**i**rd right. ......

4 You're s**u**pposed to make my life easier! / I've pl**u**gged in my laptop. ......

5 Starting with my analys**i**s of the current market. / Now I need a new m**i**crophone. ......

6 There seems to be a problem with the images on the scr**ee**n. / There are photos of a young child on the b**ea**ch. ......

B 🔊 **14.2 Listen and check. Practise saying the sentences.**

Vocabulary Builder Quiz 14 (OVB pp54–56)

Try the OVB quiz for Unit 14. Write your answers in your notebook. Then check them and record your score.

A Cross out the noun that is not possible in each set.

1 click on — an icon / a file / a cable

2 open — a file / a switch / an attachment

3 delete — a key / some text / a file

4 switch on — a light / a computer / a bulb

5 format — a plug / a document / a file

B Choose the correct words.

1 There have been huge changes in *technological / technology* in the last 10 years.

2 I tried turning the computer off and on but it didn't *do / make* any difference.

3 Don't forget to *back / save* up all your work as you go along.

4 I need to plug in my laptop. Where's the nearest *network / socket*?

5 Please don't *switch / leave* the TV on standby all night.

6 Can you *run / use* your keyboard off batteries?

C Correct one letter in the underlined words.

1 We would like to install <u>polar</u> panels in our new house.

2 He <u>spelled</u> coffee all over my desk and didn't even clear it up.

3 Can you turn the <u>ban</u> on–it's boiling in here.

4 Be careful you don't <u>trap</u> on the edge of the carpet there.

5 Remember to <u>lot</u> off when you have finished using my computer.

6 How long do you think would it take to <u>scar</u> these colour photos?

7 I love my new laptop. It's got some really <u>fool</u> programs.

8 There was a <u>litter</u> dispute about money between the two families that lasted over five years.

D Which word can you add to form compound nouns?

1 a computer / a window ....

2 an AIDS / a flu ....

3 a TV / computer ....

4 brain / computer ....

5 keyboard / people ....

6 admin / teaching ....

Score ___/25

Wait a couple of weeks and try the quiz again. Compare your scores.

15 INJURIES AND ILLNESS

VOCABULARY Injuries and illness

A Complete the conversations with the words in the boxes.

| painkillers | sneezing | a nasty cold | thermometer |

1 A: Are you OK?
   B: Yeah, I've just got ...., that's all. I can't stop
      ....
   A: Do you feel hot? Shall I get the .... to take your
      temperature?
   B: No, thanks. I'm sure it'll clear up in a couple of days. I'll just take
      some .... for my headache.

| medicine | coughing | flu | allergy |

2 A: I didn't sleep at all last night. My little boy was .... for
      hours.
   B: Poor thing. Has he got .... ?
   A: No, he has an .... to dogs. He must have been playing
      with my neighbour's puppy.
   B: That must be a worry.
   A: Don't worry. He'll be fine if he takes his .... for a
      couple of days.

| support | dizzy | stitches | sprained |

3 A: Sorry, Bill, I won't make it into work today. I've had an accident.
   B: Oh, no. What happened?
   A: Well, I felt ...., and I fell and .... my ankle.
   B: Oh dear. Is your foot in plaster?
   A: No, it's just in a .... because it isn't broken. But I also
      ended up with five .... – I cut my head when I fell.
   B: Poor you. Just stay at home until you feel better.

B Choose the correct words.

1 Whenever I eat shellfish, I come out in a nasty *rash / itchy*.
2 They thought my wrist was broken and so I had it *X-rayed / X-ray*.
3 Don't cover your cut, just keep it clean and get your mum to put *a
   bandage / some cream* on it.
4 I spent the whole weekend throwing up. What a time to get an
   upset stomach / a stomach ache!
5 The doctor said I had *high blood pressure / a chest infection*. That's
   why I kept feeling dizzy.
6 The knife slipped when I was preparing the vegetables and I got a
   nasty *bump / cut* on my hand.
7 I can move my foot OK but I can't get my shoe on because it's
   really *stiff / swollen*.
8 I'd hate to suffer from *migraines / arthritis*. It must be awful not to
   be able to use your hands.
9 There's no point asking the doctor for *allergies / antibiotics*. They
   don't work for colds.

DEVELOPING CONVERSATIONS
Short questions with *any*

**Complete the conversations with the questions in
the box.**

Any pain?	Any itchiness?	Any dizziness?
Any stiffness?	Any vomiting?	Any questions?
Any medication?	Any other symptoms?	

1 A: So, what can I do for you this morning?
   B: Well, I don't feel too good, doctor. I slipped and
      banged my head earlier this morning.
   A: Right. ....
   B: Yes, I feel like the room is spinning when I stand
      up.
   A: OK. ....
   B: Yes, the back of my head really hurts.
   A: I see. ....
   B: No, not really, I can move my neck fine.
   A: OK. Let's get you X-rayed to check everything is
      OK. ....
   B: Yes, just one. How long will the X-ray take? I'm
      supposed to be at work.

2 A: Oh, hello. I'm calling about my little boy. He's
      allergic to dairy products but he drank some milk
      at school by mistake.
   B: I see. ....
   A: Yes, he threw up just once, about half an hour ago.
   B: OK. ....
   A: No, he hasn't been scratching or anything.
   B: ....
   A: Just one. He's been coughing quite a lot.
   B: OK, that's probably unrelated.
      ....
   A: No, he doesn't take anything and I haven't given
      him any medicine.
   B: OK, you'd better bring him in to see me.
   A I can see him at the end of surgery this morning.
      Would 12:30 be OK?

LISTENING

🔊 15.1 You are going to hear four short conversations. Listen and choose the correct answer to the questions, a, b or c.

1 Where has the woman hurt herself?

2 What two symptoms does the woman have?

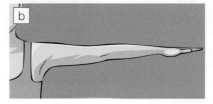

3 What treatment does the man advise?

4 What is the man allergic to?

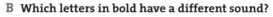

PRONUNCIATION Vowel sounds

A 🔊 15.2 Listen to the sentences from Listening. Circle the correct symbol for the letters in bold.

1 I can't stop c**ou**ghing.   /ɜː/   /ɒ/
2 Let me have a l**oo**k.   /ʊ/   /uː/
3 It's a tiny c**u**t.   /ʌ/   /ʊ/
4 You don't need a band**a**ge.   /æ/   /ɪ/
5 He sent me for some t**e**sts.   /e/   /ə/
6 It turns out I have an all**e**rgy. /ɜː/   /ə/
7 Why do you keep getting a r**a**sh? /æ/   /ɑː/

B Which letters in bold have a different sound?

1 d**i**zzy ant**i**biotics st**i**ff **i**tchy
2 b**u**mp c**u**t bl**oo**d press**ure**
3 stom**a**ch b**a**ndage r**a**sh **a**llergy
4 c**ou**gh d**o**ctor sw**o**llen g**o**t
5 m**e**dicine h**ea**dache f**ee**l inf**e**ction
6 **ar**thritis temperat**ure** brok**e**n medicat**io**n
7 sh**ou**ld sh**ou**lder g**oo**d p**u**lled

C 🔊 15.3 Listen to the words in exercise B and check.

VOCABULARY Word formation

Complete the text with the correct form of the words in brackets.

In general, I think I'm pretty healthy. I don't have any serious [1] .... (medicine) conditions and I hardly ever suffer from [2] .... (virus) infections or bugs. I'm lucky because I'm [3] .... (natural) quite slim and I am not really into [4] .... (fat) or fried foods. But, I do have one terrible secret – I'm [5] .... (addictive) to chocolate. I've been a chocoholic since I first tried the stuff when I was a child. Of course, I've tried to give it up but it seems that I am [6] .... (cure) – I have to have at least one bar of chocolate a day. And if I cut down, the people around me can't stand my [7] .... (irritable) and so they rush out and buy me some. And it seems that the love of chocolate can be [8] .... (infection). My flatmate didn't use to have a sweet tooth but now she's as much a chocoholic as me.

VOCABULARY

Explaining causes and results

A Choose the correct words. Then decide if you think the sentences are true or false.

Heath matters – myth or reality?

People are always giving us advice on keeping safe and staying healthy but how much of it is true?

1 Cutting down on salt can lead *to* / *for* a reduction in blood pressure.

2 Headaches are *link* / *linked* to high blood pressure.

3 Having a flu injection can make you *to get* / *get* flu.

4 Taking a lot of vitamin C doesn't *lead* / *mean* you won't catch a cold.

5 Shaving hair *makes* / *causes* it to grow back faster and darker.

6 Drinking warm milk makes you *go* / *that you go* to sleep more easily.

7 Staring at an eclipse of the sun can *lead* / *make* you blind.

8 Bad eyesight can be caused *from* / *by* sitting too close to the TV.

READING

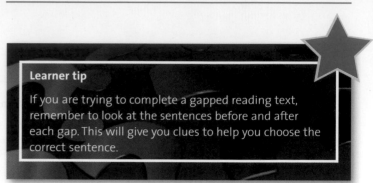

Learner tip

If you are trying to complete a gapped reading text, remember to look at the sentences before and after each gap. This will give you clues to help you choose the correct sentence.

A Read the article quickly. The first sentence of each paragraph has been removed. Write the correct letter (a–e) in the gaps in the article.

a Scientific research shows that Okinawans actually age more slowly than other human beings.

b The typical daily calorie count in Okinawa is about 1 200.

c It's this ability to trick their bodies into starvation that may be keeping Okinawans physiologically so young.

d Thanks to advances in medical science, we are all living longer and healthier lives.

e It isn't easy to explain why these people live so long.

B Read the article again. Decide if these sentences are true (T) or false (F), or if the article doesn't say (DS).

1 On average, men in Britain live longer than women.

2 Okinawa has four times as many people over 100 as Britain or the United States.

3 Women in Okinawa live longer than men.

4 Okinawans' bodies stay young for longer than other nationalities'.

5 Many Okinawans live a long time but also have a lot of health problems.

6 Okinawans stop eating before they are really full.

7 A calorie-reduced diet leads to long life in all nationalities.

8 Scientists have worked out why Okinawans live longer than other people.

9 Japanese supermarkets don't have many special offers.

C Complete the sentences with the missing prepositions. Look back at the article if you need to.

1 If you eat a range .... foods every day, that will help you have a healthy diet.

2 I think the secret .... good health is to have a good diet and drink plenty of water.

3 In stark contrast .... our ancestors, most people now get very little exercise.

4 If you cook all meat thoroughly, there is little danger .... getting food poisoning.

5 Despite advances .... medicine, there is still no cure for the common cold.

6 There is a huge difference .... the Western and Japanese diet.

The **time** of your **life**

… But there are places in the world where people live longer than anywhere else. The remote Japanese island of Okinawa is one of these places. Located southwest of mainland Japan, Okinawa is one of a chain of islands that stretch down towards Taiwan. The average lifespan in Britain is 77 years for men and 81 for women. Okinawa has a population of about one million, of which 900 are centenarians – four times higher than the average in Britain or the USA. So what is their secret of long life?

… "The calendar may say they're 70 but their body says they're 50," says Bradley Willcox, a scientist researching the extraordinary phenomenon. "The most impressive part of it is that a good lot of them are healthy until the very end."

… Research has shown hormonal differences between Okinawans and the rest of the population but their longevity has also been linked to diet. They eat more tofu and soya products than any other people in the world and also enjoy a range of different fruit and vegetables, all rich in anti-oxidants. But the most significant thing isn't what they eat, but how much. The Okinawans have a cultural tradition known as 'hara hachi bu', which translates as 'eat until you are only 80% full'.

… That's about 20% less than most people in the UK. Scientists refer to this way of eating as 'caloric restriction'. No-one knows exactly why it works, but scientists believe it sends a signal to the body that there is the danger of famine. This in turn makes the body protect itself and so may lead to better preservation and slower aging.

"… It's a stark contrast with the cultural habits that drive food consumption in other parts of the world," says Mr Willcox. If you look at high streets and supermarkets in most Western cities, you will see that he is right. Restaurants offer all-you-can-eat menus and supersize portions. Supermarkets are full of special offers encouraging us to buy more food than we need.

Glossary

centenarian: a person who is 100 years old or older
longevity: long life
anti-oxidants: substances thought to protect body cells from the damaging effects of oxidation (combining with oxygen)
famine: an extreme lack of food

Language note noun and preposition

Many nouns, especially abstract nouns, are followed by a specific preposition, e.g.
*There's been an **increase in** the number of people over 100. We should all take **responsibility for** our own health.*
Remember to record noun + preposition collocations in your vocabulary notebook.

VOCABULARY Accidents and problems

Complete the conversations with the correct form of the verbs in the boxes.

crash into	ended up with sunburn
fall down	bite

1 A: Have you ever had a bad accident?
   B: No, I think I've been quite lucky. The worst thing was when I was about 12 and I .... the stairs at school. I had an X-ray but everything was fine. What about you?
   A: Oh, I'm an accident waiting to happen.
   B: What makes you say that?
   A: Well, on holiday last month, I .... after just an hour on the beach. Then I was walking back to the hotel and a dog went mad and .... me. Then the taxi that was taking me to hospital .... a bus and I had to walk the last kilometre!

faint	get food poisoning	slip on	sting

2 A: Hi, I haven't seen you for ages. How are things?
   B: Not great, actually. I was off sick last week. A bee .... me on my cheek when I was at a barbecue and half my face swelled up. Then I .... after eating some undercooked meat.
   A: You poor thing.
   B: You haven't heard the whole story. I ended up in hospital after I .... some water on the kitchen floor and banged my head. Everyone thought I ....after the shock of the sting, but it was just an accident.
   A: What a nightmare! I hope you're OK now.

bruise	burn	fall off	trip over

3 A: Kim was telling me that Nick has had an accident.
   B: Yes, he .... his hand while he was trying to put out a fire.
   A: Oh, no! What happened?
   B: A candle .... the shelf on to the carpet and set it on fire. And then he .... the lamp cable when he was rushing to get some water.
   A: How scary! Is he OK?
   B: Yes, I think so. He .... his knee when he fell, but it's nothing too serious. His hand is getting better and there's no real damage to the house.

GRAMMAR Reported speech

Change the sentences into reported speech.

1 'I'm not allergic to antibiotics.'
   The woman said ....

2 'The operation will last about an hour.'
   The surgeon said ....

3 'I usually take the medicine at night.'
   The man said ....

4 'We're waiting for our son's test results.'
   The parents said ....

5 'I've broken my leg in a skiing accident.'
   The boy said ....

6 'We're going to X-ray his ankle as soon as possible.'
   The nurses said ....

7 'The dog bit me on the arm.'
   The girl said ....

8 'You can visit Melanie whenever you like'.
   The doctor said ....

9 'You must make an appointment for tests at the hospital'.
   The doctor said ....

GRAMMAR Reporting verbs

Choose the correct verb in brackets to report the sentences.

1 'I'm sorry I didn't visit you in hospital.' (apologise for / threaten)
   He apologised for not visiting me in hospital
   ....

2 'I really must check your blood pressure.' (insist on / advise)
   The doctor ....
   ....

3 'I didn't give the patient the wrong medication.' (refuse / deny)
   The nurse ....
   ....

4 'I'll look after everything while you're in hospital.' (promise / persuade)
   My neighbour ....
   ....

5 'I'll get your tablets for you.' (recommend / offer)
   She ....
   ....

6 'Don't sunbathe for more than half an hour, Ruth.' (tell / admit)
   Mum ....
   ....

7 'Why don't you try yoga to help with stress?' (claim / suggest)
   My friend ....
   ....

8 'Don't eat or drink anything before your operation.' (agree / warn)
   The surgeon ....
   ....

DEVELOPING WRITING

An email – describing an accident / problem

A **Read Lucy's email quickly. Number the content of her message in order.**

the situation before the problem happened ......

the doctor's diagnosis ......

how she feels now ......

how she got to hospital ......

the people who helped her ......

what she was doing when the problem happened ......

B **Complete the email with the verb forms in the box.**

set off	would need	insisted	were eating
ended up	set off	'd left	offered
stood up	persuaded	'll be going out	

```
●●○

Hi Max

Thanks for your note. You wanted to know how I
¹ ............................. in hospital? It's a long story, but
here goes…

We were on a walking holiday and, on the last day, we
² ............................. early while it was still quite
cool. I ³............................. my hat and suncream
at the hotel but I didn't think I ⁴ .............................
them. I've always been fine in hot weather. Anyway,
by lunchtime, I was very red and sore but we were in
the middle of nowhere, so there wasn't much I could
do about it.

While we ⁵ ............................. lunch on the cliff top,
the sun was absolutely scorching. Just as I
⁶ ............................. to continue the walk, I felt
really dizzy and then I fainted. It was so embarrassing!
Fortunately, there was a group of walkers with a guide
and they ⁷ ............................. to help. I
⁸ ............................. that I was OK but the guide
⁹ ............................. me to go to hospital. The next
thing I knew I was in an air ambulance. The doctor
diagnosed me with sunstroke and severe dehydration
– what a nightmare!

I'm fine now but I don't think I ¹⁰ .............................
in the sun again any time soon

Love
Lucy
```

C **Write an email (120–150 words) starting with these words.**

*Thanks for your note. You wanted to know how I
ended up in hospital? Well, it's a long story, but
here goes …*

Vocabulary Builder Quiz 15 (*OVB* pp58–60)

Try the *OVB* quiz for Unit 15. Write your answers in your notebook. Then check them and record your score.

A **Which word is the odd one out in each set?**

1	infection	antibiotics	painkillers	medication
2	malaria	stimulant	diarrhoea	arthritis
3	acne	rash	sneeze	sunburn
4	sprain	blood	chest	joints

B **Which preposition is missing in each sentence?**

1 It's very easy to become addicted .... cigarettes.

2 She broke her arm when she fell .... the stairs at home.

3 Adding more memory should speed .... your computer.

4 I fell .... the horse the first time I went riding.

5 Please put your shoes away. I nearly fell .... them.

C **Find words that are both nouns and verbs to complete the sentences.**

1 I've got a really sore throat and a .... I can't stand smoky places. They always make me ....

2 I was terrified. I thought the bear was going to .... me. He was arrested for a violent .... on another student.

3 Scientists have never found a .... for the common cold. It's going to take a long time to .... the disease.

4 This insect .... is really itchy. Don't worry. The dog won't .... you. He's really gentle.

5 My arm was swollen for hours after I had a bee .... If you just stay still, the insect won't .... you.

D **Which word do you need to complete the sentences in each pair?**

1 The .... affected the whole computer network. I think I'm coming down with a ....

2 He's been diagnosed with heart .... He's suffering from an incurable ....

3 What are the .... of malaria? What .... do you have, apart from a sore throat?

4 Kim has got a .... cough at the moment. I need something for this .... rash on my chest.

E **Match the question halves.**

1	Have you ever had any adverse	a	your finger joints?
2	How long did it take for you to	b	symptoms when you gave up coffee?
3	Why do you keep cracking	c	my blood pressure?
4	How did you get	d	reactions to taking antibiotics?
5	Do I need to lower	e	medical condition?
6	Did you suffer many withdrawal	f	such a good tan?
7	Have you ever had a serious	g	regain consciousness?

Score ___ /25

Wait a couple of weeks and try the quiz again. Compare your scores.

VOCABULARY Newspapers

A **Which part of a newspaper are these people talking about? Match 1–8 and a–h.**

1 international news   ......
2 the business pages   ......
3 the reviews   ......
4 the gossip pages   ......
5 the letters page   ......
6 national news   ......
7 the horoscopes   ......
8 the sports pages   ......

a I never read them. How can they give a prediction that fits millions of different people?

b I always turn to the back of the paper. I have to check out what's happening in the league.

c I check them about once a week. I think it's important to see what's happening in the world of commerce.

d I read them if I've seen the same film or play – just to see if I agree.

e I tend to read about what's happening at home rather than stories from other countries.

f I know none of it is serious, but I can't resist finding out what's happening to the celebrities.

g I don't read them very often. Most people who write in have very extreme opinions – they never give a balanced view.

h I read all of it – it's important to keep up with what's happening around the world.

B **Complete the questions with the words in the box.**

the score   star sign   ceasefire   exchange rate   premiere marks out of ten

1 A: What's the .... with the dollar?
   B: It's gone down. It's only $1.45 to the pound.
2 A: Put the news on. I want to see which celebrities turn up to the movie .... ?
   B: That's not news. I'm not interested in all that celebrity stuff.
3 A: What's the latest news from the war zone? Have they agreed a ....
4 A: How many .... did they give the film?
   B: Only five. Is it still worth going to see it?
5 A: Pass me the paper. I want to see .... from last night's match.
   B: Don't tell me. I'm going to watch it on TV later.
6 A: What .... are you?
   B: Scorpio, but I never read my horoscope.

DEVELOPING CONVERSATIONS
Apparently

Complete the conversations with the lines in the box. There are two lines that you don't need.

Apparently, in patient tests it was 90 per cent successful.
Apparently, they won the race in record time.
Apparently, it doesn't use electricity or gas for heating or for any of the equipment.
Apparently, rates of diabetes have risen by 25%.
Apparently, it sold out in less than five minutes.
Apparently, the Arctic ice is disappearing more quickly than ever before.
Apparently, she'd never been abroad before.

1 A: Did you read about that new laptop that costs only £100?
   B: Yeah, it sounds like a real bargain, doesn't it?
   ....
2 A: Did you see that thing in the paper about the new eco-house they've built?
   B: No, what was that?
   A: ....
3 A: Did you hear about that new treatment for colds?
   B: Yeah, amazing, isn't it. ....
4 A: Did you see that interview with the woman who travelled round the world at the age of 90?
   B: Yes, wasn't she an inspiration? ....
5 A: Did you see that thing on TV about climate change?
   B: No, what was that?
   A: ....

Learner tip

Don't forget to look back at the *Developing conversations* sections in your Student's Book to remind you of the expressions that you can use in everyday conversation.

LISTENING

A 🔊 **16.1** Look at the photo. Do you know where this event took place? Listen to the first paragraph of the news story and check.

B 🔊 **16.2** Listen to the news story and complete the notes.

```
US CRASH CAUSED BY BIRDS

Flight information
US Airways Flight ¹ ......1549......
Crash location: Hudson River
Date: ² .....................
No. of passengers and crew: 155
No. of survivors: ³ .....................

Left LaGuardia Airport: 15:26 for Charlotte, North
Carolina
Time in the air: ⁴ .....................
Top altitude: ⁵ ..................... feet (975 metres)

Crash details
Landed in water at: 15:30
Only injuries: one person with ⁶ .....................
Last person to leave: Captain Sullenberger
Described as hero by: mayor, governor, and former
⁷ .....................

Problems with birds
Frequency of problem: every ⁸ ..................... but
planes can take the impact
Events in the news when: large flocks or large
birds hit at critical moment
Type of bird hit Flight 1549: Canada geese
Weight: 1.5- ⁹ ..................... kilos
No. of reported bird strikes: ¹⁰ .....................
between 1990 and ¹¹ ..................... .
No. of deaths: ¹² ..................... since 1988
Cost of damage: $ ¹³ .....................
```

PRONUNCIATION Numbers

A **How do you read the numbers and years in bold? Choose *a* or *b*.**

1 Flight **1549**
   a one five four nine
   b one thousand five hundred and forty-nine
2 **155** passengers
   a one hundred fifty-five
   b one hundred and fifty-five
3 **3200** feet
   a three thousand two hundred
   b three thousand and two hundred
4 **975** metres
   a nine hundreds and seventy-five
   b nine hundred and seventy-five
5 **5.5** kilos
   a five point five
   b five comma five
6 **76,000** reports
   a seventy-six thousands
   b seventy-six thousand
7 since **1988**
   a one thousand nine hundred and eighty-eight
   b nineteen eighty-eight
8 **600,000,000** dollars
   a six hundreds million
   b six hundred million

B 🔊 **16.3** Listen and check your answers.

C Listen again and mark the main stresses on the correct answers in exercise A.

D Practise saying the numbers and years.

Language note reading numbers

- There is no plural *-s* after *hundred, thousand, million,* and *billion* when part of a number: *six **thousand** and twenty.*
- We usually use *and* in numbers over a hundred to link hundreds and tens: *nine hundred* and *ninety-nine. And* is often left out in American English.
- Years up to 2000 are read differently from numbers:
   1666 = sixteen sixty-six (not *one thousand six hundred* and *sixty-six*)
   2012 = two thousand and twelve *or* twenty twelve
- The full stop in decimals is read as point:
   1.732 = one point seven three two

VOCABULARY
Explaining who people are

A Match the sentence halves.

1 Aung San Suu Kyi is a political activist who
2 Charles Babbage was an English mathematician who
3 Idi Amin was a military dictator in Uganda who
4 Robert Koch was a German doctor who
5 Haile Gebrselassie is an Ethiopian athlete who
6 Gregor Mendel was an Austrian scientist who

a is considered the father of genetics.
b won the Nobel Prize for Medicine for his work on tuberculosis.
c set the world record for the marathon in 2009.
d campaigns for the rights of people in Myanmar (Burma).
e developed the idea of a programmable computer.
f is said to be responsible for the deaths of hundreds of thousands of people.

B Read the quiz. Choose the correct words.

¿WHO'S WHO?

1 Q Who was Francisco Goya?
  A A Spanish *paint / artist* who *considers / is considered* by many the *foinder / father* of modern art.

2 Q Who was Simón Bolívar?
  A A South American independence leader. He *lead / led* the liberation struggle from Spanish control and was the *founder / finder* of Bolivia.

3 Q Who was Mahatma Ghandi?
  A An *activist / active* who *campaigner / campaigned* for independence and the *writes / rights* of people in India.

4 Q Who was Edward Jenner?
  A An English *doctor / medical* who developed a *virus / vaccine* against smallpox.

5 Q Who was Isaac Newton?
  A An English *mathematics / mathematician* *whose / which* most famous work was on motion and gravity.

6 Q Who's Barbora Špotáková?
  A A Czech *athletic / athlete* who *set / put* the world record for women's javelin in 2008.

7 Q Who was 'Papa Doc' Duvalier?
  A A *dictate / dictator* in Haiti in the 1960s. He was thought to be *responsible / responsibility* for 30,000 deaths and the exile of thousands more.

8 Q Who was Howard Carter?
  A A British archaeologist who *studies / studied* Ancient Egypt and *developed / discovered* the tomb of Tutankhamun.

GRAMMAR Defining relative clauses

A Complete the sentences with the endings in the box.

1 It's an educational scheme ....
2 He's the fashion designer ....
3 It's the place in Washington ....
4 She's a soul singer ....
5 It's the night of the 31st October ....
6 It's the store in London ....
7 It's an American government organisation ....
8 It was the period of time ....

a when unfriendly relations existed between the Soviet Union and the West.
b where the President of the USA lives.
c that enables students to study abroad for part of their degree.
d whose most famous song is probably *Respect*.
e when people dress up as witches, ghosts, etc.
f where you are supposed to be able to buy anything.
g which is responsible for space research.
h who created a style called 'the New Look'.

B Match the descriptions (1–8) in exercise A with the topics below.

Christian Dior ......   the Cold War ......   Halloween ......
ERASMUS ......   Harrods ......   NASA ......
Aretha Franklin ......   the White House ......

C Complete the sentences with appropriate relative pronouns. Give alternative answers where possible.

1 Michael Phelps is the swimmer *who / that* won eight gold medals in the Beijing Olympics.
2 Darwin's *Origin of Species* is one of the books .... changed the world.
3 10 Downing Street is the house .... the British Prime Minister lives and works.
4 Lance Armstrong is the cyclist .... illness didn't stop him winning the Tour de France.
5 Martin Luther King Day is .... Americans celebrate their most important human rights activist.
6 JK Rowling is the writer .... is supposed to have encouraged boys to read more.
7 Oxfam is a charity .... has worked to help people all over the world.
8 Leonardo da Vinci is the artist .... painting the *Mona Lisa* is supposed to be the most famous in the world.

D In which three sentences can you leave out the relative pronoun?

1 I remember the day when Barack Obama became president.
2 What is the news event which will have the most important effects around the world?
3 I'll never forget the moment when I saw my hero on stage.
4 The scientist who has changed technology most was probably Tim Berners-Lee, the inventor of the World Wide Web.
5 Coca-Cola is a brand that is recognised all over the world.
6 What happened to the singer that you voted for on the talent show?

DEVELOPING WRITING A website entry – an influential person

A Read the text quickly. Choose the best summary of Jonathan Ive.

A designer who

a has designed a new computer and won an award.

b has been very important in computer programming.

c has affected many people's lives but who doesn't want to be famous.

B Choose the correct words.

Jonathan Ive,
British designer

[1] *Despite / Although* not a household name, Jonathan Ive is responsible [2] *for / of* a revolution in the world of technology. He's the British designer [3] *who / which* transformed the computer from a boring tool into a lifestyle experience [4] *where / when* he designed the first iMac in 1999. It's hard to remember that before the iMac the world was full of beige desktop computers that weren't particularly user-friendly. The iMac was [5] *no / not* only good to look at but also easy to use. It also gave technology a more universal [6] *attract / appeal* by encouraging greater female interest in computers.

Jonathan Ive has also re-invented the [7] *way / form* we listen to music and use the phone with his work as principle designer of the iPod and the iPhone at the technology company, Apple. He had been [8] *known / called* an original thinker and one of the most [9] *influential / influence* designers on the planet. This is because his products aren't just old things re-designed to look new – they really are new.

Ive has received a range of [10] *presents / awards* including The Design Museum's Designer of the Year in both 2002 and 2003. Despite his considerable talent and achievements, he [11] *keeps / remains* a modest man who doesn't chase praise or celebrity. He always emphasises the teamwork [12] *who / that* goes into the products for which he receives recognition and fame.

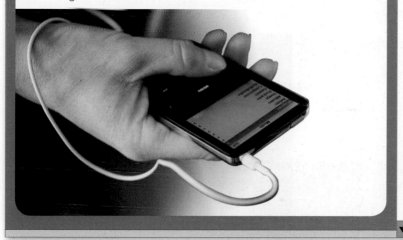

C Complete the sentences with the verbs in the box. Then match the sentences (1–8) to the people (a–h).

inspired	was
raised	led
left	dedicated
was	revolutionised

He / She ...

1 .... the people to independence.

2 .... the way people dress.

3 .... an inspiration to everyone in the team.

4 .... a lasting mark on the world of classical composing.

5 .... millions of pounds for people in the third world.

6 .... his / her time to finding a cure for cancer.

7 .... a pioneer in the field of modern ballet.

8 .... huge numbers of people to care about the world.

a a charity worker

b a politician

c a scientist

d a sportsman / woman

e a dancer

f an environmentalist

g a musician

h a clothes designer

D A website called *People to remember* has been created to celebrate people who have had some lasting influence. Write a short profile (120–150 words) of someone famous from your country to appear on the website. Choose from these ideas or use an idea of your own.

- a politician
- a sports person
- a performer
- an artist

READING

A Read the article quickly. Match the stunts to their intended audience.

1 The peanut protester   ......
2 Anything is possible at Harrods   ......
3 Earth Hour   ......
4 Michael Jackson on the Thames   ......
5 The colour of Pepsi   ......

a music fans
b people who are concerned about the environment
c people who prefer Coca-Cola
d a politician
e people who have a lot of money to spend

B Read the article again. Which of these statements are true, according to the article?

1 Mark McGowan wanted to draw attention to the amount of money he owed at the end of his course. ☐
2 The Harrods customer bought a helicopter from the store. ☐
3 Harrods weren't able to fulfil all their customers' wishes. ☐
4 Since the launch of Earth Hour, the number of people taking part has doubled. ☐
5 Public buildings and spaces all over the world have taken part in Earth Hour. ☐
6 Sony used a similar campaign for Michael Jackson's CD in different countries. ☐
7 Pepsi wanted to promote a change in the formula of its drink. ☐
8 Pepsi devised a range of stunts in its campaign. ☐

C Look at the highlighted words in the article. What do they refer to?

five = publicity stunts

D Choose the correct words. Look back at the article if you need to.

1 Understanding some publicity stunts is easier said than done. It's hard to know sometimes the point people are trying to *make / do*.
2 I don't understand celebrities who *carry / catch* the public's attention all the time and then complain about it.
3 Publicity is very short-lived. Stunts that create massive *media / medium* interest one day are forgotten the next.
4 Companies are spending more and more money to help promote the *start / launch* of new products.
5 Publicity can be used to *raise / rise* awareness of serious issues like climate change.
6 Advertisers use a range of techniques to capture the public's *imagination / imagine* in different countries.
7 It amazes me when a company sets up a big *promotional / promotion* campaign for a product that isn't very good.
8 Why do companies spend so much money to *promote / promotion* the change of a product that people were already happy with?

Publicity at any price

Have you ever wondered how far some people will go to get noticed or to make their point? There are hundred of examples of publicity stunts but here are just **five** that really caught the public's attention.

1 THE PEANUT PROTESTER

In September 2003, Mark McGowan created massive media interest when he took two weeks to push a peanut across London, using only his nose. The protest against his student debt started at Goldsmiths College and ended at 10 Downing Street, where Mr McGowan delivered the nut to former Prime Minister Tony Blair. **He** asked Mr Blair to accept the nut as payment for **his** debt.

2 ANYTHING IS POSSIBLE AT HARRODS

A team from luxury department store Harrods used over 600 metres of paper to gift-wrap a helicopter in September 2006. The helicopter was chartered from Air Harrods by a customer who wanted to take his partner on the trip of a lifetime. The customer asked for **it** to be gift-wrapped to make **it** extra special. The stunt was filmed to help promote the launch of Harrod's 'Anything Is Possible' season.

3 EARTH HOUR

In 2007, Sydney, Australia saw the launch of **this** campaign to raise awareness of climate change. 2.2 million homes and businesses turned off their non-essential lights for one hour. Since **then**, this event has captured the public's imagination with up to 50 million people across the world taking part. Global landmarks like the Golden Gate Bridge in San Francisco, Rome's Colosseum and the Coca-Cola billboard in Time's Square have all stood in darkness.

4 MICHAEL JACKSON ON THE THAMES

The release of Michael Jackson's CD HIStory was marked by his record company, Sony, by floating a huge statue of **the artist** down the River Thames in June 1995. This was part of a massive promotional campaign costing $30 million. There were a total of nine statues used in countries throughout Europe as part of the campaign. Each **one** was 10 metres tall, 2100 kilos in weight and was made from steel and fibreglass.

5 THE COLOUR OF PEPSI

To promote the change of packaging colour from red and white to blue, the soft drink company, Pepsi, launched a series of ambitious publicity stunts. In April 2006 **it** paid the British newspaper, *The Mirror*, to print on blue paper. It also arranged for Concorde to be sprayed blue and got the cosmonauts on the Mir space station to be filmed with a giant Pepsi can. In total the campaign cost the company £300 million.

Glossary

student debt: the amount a student has to pay back after receiving loans to fund his / her studies
chartered: hired for private use
fibreglass: a light, hard substance used for making boats, containers, etc.
Concorde: the first supersonic passenger jet
Mir space station: the world's first research station in space

Vocabulary Builder Quiz 16 (*OVB* pp62–64)

Try the *OVB* quiz for Unit 16. Write your answers in your notebook. Then check them and record your score.

A Match 1–5 and a–e to form compound nouns.
1 talent   a sign
2 star   b premiere
3 film   c show
4 exchange   d rate
5 research   e grant

B Complete the words with the correct suffix.
1 The police officer won an award for brave............ after he rescued a child.
2 The 30-year dictator............ ended when the leader died.
3 Hundreds of people in manufacturing are facing redundan..............
4 His grandfather fought for the libera............ of his country from occupation.
5 Who is the most influen............ politician in your country at the moment?
6 I've been a member of an athlet............ club for the last year.
7 The country was unif............ after a long military campaign.
8 She was very courag............ throughout her illness.

C Find words that are both nouns and verbs to complete the sentences.
1 We need to .... these signs to the wall.
   Can I use a .... to hang this mirror up?
2 It's will be impossible to .... all these pieces of glass back together.
   Where's the ....? I need to repair this broken vase.
3 Have you got a paper .... I could use?
   Please .... all the documents together so that I don't lose any.
4 Have we got any ....? I need to wrap up all my Christmas presents.
   I need to .... this envelope down. The glue has gone dry and it won't stick.

D Choose the correct words.
1 Who had a *hit / tune* with the CD *Back to Black*?
2 They named the airport *from / after* John Lennon.
3 Our business was *found / founded* over 100 years ago.
4 Elvis *considers / is considered* to be the king of rock and roll.
5 What do the *reviews / records* say about the new James Bond film?
6 What is the biggest *attacker / barrier* to success at school?
7 My sister was a *contestant / competition* on a talent show.
8 It was a shame to see the oldest shop in town had closed *off / down*.

Score ____ /25

Wait a couple of weeks and try the quiz again.
Compare your scores.

AUDIOSCRIPT

UNIT 01

1.1

A = Andy, T = Trisha

A: Hi Trisha, how are things?

T: Yeah, fine, thanks. In fact I've got some news for you.

A: Oh yes?

T: I've left my job and I've signed up for a building course.

A: Er ... run that by me again.

T: A building course ... at the local technical college. I wanted a new challenge.

A: OK, so most women do an evening course in a foreign language or knitting or whatever, but you want to learn building skills?

T: And why not? More and more women are going into construction. And there's a need for builders and plumbers.

A: Listen, I'm not criticising, in fact I admire you. It's hard to try something new.

T: Mmm, well the first class was a bit nerve wracking. I wasn't the *only* woman there but it was *nearly* all men. We had to explain why we were on the course but my mind went blank. And then I said, 'I'm really interested in houses and I want to know how they work.' I felt such a fool and I went bright red.

A: Oh dear.

T: But then *no one* came up with very clever reasons.

A: Hmm. So, what does the course involve?

T: Well, the first term is basic techniques and then we get to choose electrics, plumbing, bricklaying, or whatever.

A: What are you going to do?

T: I fancy plumbing. I think it's quite creative. I'd rather work on people's houses than sit in an office all day. And there are plenty of jobs advertised in the paper and online. Plus have you seen how much plumbers charge? I'm going to make a fortune.

A: Good for you! Any chance of a discount for friends?

1.2

A = Andy, T = Trisha

1 T: I've signed up for a building course.

2 A: ...an evening course in a foreign language or knitting or whatever

3 T: There's a need for builders and plumbers.

4 T: The first class was a bit nerve-wracking.

5 T: I felt such a fool and I went bright red.

UNIT 02

2.1

M = Mark, D = Mrs deVere, A = Annie

M: Well, I'm not normally a nervous person, so I felt pretty relaxed about the whole thing. And I've always got on well with people, so I didn't expect there to be a problem. But things started going wrong from the moment I turned up. I was wearing jeans and a shirt, but the restaurant was a really elegant place. Her mum was in a silk dress and her dad in a smart suit. I was really fed up with Annie that she hadn't warned me it was a formal dinner. Anyway, I tried to make conversation but I kept getting confused when anyone asked me a question. Then I told a couple of jokes and no one laughed. The silence was awful. Annie said her parents didn't mind, but it was a relief when the evening was over.

D: Mark and Annie had been going out together for about six months. She never talked about him much so we had no idea of what to expect. To be honest, we hadn't been very keen on most of her boyfriends, so my husband and I were rather worried about the dinner. It was difficult when he first arrived because we were wearing smart clothes but he was in jeans. He was obviously embarrassed. I think Annie had forgotten to tell him that we were meeting in a formal restaurant. Anyway, we all had a drink and relaxed a little. He seemed rather nervous and told one or two awful jokes, but all in all it was a good evening. In fact, we were pleased that Annie had found someone nice.

A: Well, my parents have never liked any of my boyfriends so I was pretty stressed about the whole evening. Usually, my dad gets in a bad mood about something and so no one can enjoy themselves. Anyway, I felt really guilty when Mark walked in because I hadn't warned him about what to wear. He looked annoyed with me at first but then he calmed down a bit. Mark chatted with my parents but he didn't talk too much or try to impress them. I thought everything went well, even Mark's very old jokes! I was in a good mood just to see my parents spending time with my boyfriend.

2.2

1 I'm not normally a nervous person, so I felt pretty relaxed about the whole thing.

2 I was wearing jeans and a shirt, but the restaurant was a really elegant place.

3 I was really fed up with Annie that she hadn't warned me it was a formal dinner.

4 To be honest, we hadn't been very keen on most of her boyfriends, so my husband and I were rather worried about the dinner.

5 I was in a good mood just to see my parents spending time with my boyfriend.

UNIT 03

🌑 3.1
Speaker 1
We booked the holiday online. The hotel sounded wonderful from the description and the photos looked good on the website – nice quiet beaches and lots of places to visit. We were so disappointed when we got there. Everywhere was so crowded – we gave up trying to find a space on the beach. There were queues everywhere in the theme parks, and you had to wait ages to get a table in the restaurants. We ended up getting really stressed with all the crowds. The receptionist said it was quieter in the autumn but who wants to go on holiday when it's cold?

Speaker 2
It was my first holiday without my parents and I was so excited about it. I travelled with a group of friends from college. We booked a holiday apartment to share the costs of the accommodation. Things started badly because we were delayed at the airport, but things got worse when we arrived at the apartment. The owner charged us a £200 deposit in case we damaged anything. We thought we had paid the full cost when we booked. Then we got ripped off everywhere we went – the restaurants, bars, even at the city ruins. I bought some souvenirs which were half the price everywhere else. I was in such a bad mood all week.

Speaker 3
Things started so well. We got to the airport in good time and did a bit of shopping in duty free. The flight took off and landed on time so there were no transport problems, for once. Then things started to change. My friend and I couldn't agree on what to do or where to go. We spent so long planning that we didn't see much of the local area. I wanted to learn about local history – visiting the castle, Roman ruins, things like that. Sally wanted to go shopping and hang out at the theme park. My idea of hell! In the end we didn't stop arguing all week. I was so relieved to get home.

Speaker 4
We had booked a taxi to take us to the airport but the driver didn't turn up. My neighbour offered to take us, but we got stuck in a traffic jam on the motorway. We decided to divert to the nearest railway station, forgetting that there was a train strike that day. We managed to get a taxi. The driver wanted to charge double the normal price. We knew he was ripping us off but we had no choice. He got us to the terminal half an hour before take off. We thought we would be OK, but the terminal was so crowded that we had to queue. So, we missed the flight and had to wait ages for the next one. The holiday itself was OK but the journey was a nightmare from start to finish.

Speaker 5
I don't think we'll be going there again. We expected the resort to have lots of places to visit. Unfortunately, there was only a theme park and some ruins. The ruins had been a temple, according to the guidebook. But we couldn't see anything except a hole in the ground. The other problem was our hotel. It was about an hour outside of the centre and the bus service was terrible. We decided to hire a car and spend a day at the nearest lake. When we got there, there were people all along the lakeside, so we had to eat our picnic in the car! The theme park wasn't much better. It was over 100km outside of the centre and when we got there, half the rides were closed and the other ones were really old. The kids were so disappointed.

🌑 3.2
1 The hotel sounded wonderful. / The terminal was so crowded.
2 There was only a theme park. / There were queues everywhere.
3 We had booked a taxi. / I was in such a bad mood.
4 There was a train strike that day. / It was quieter in the autumn.
5 My neighbour offered to take us. / I was so relieved to get home.
6 The bus service was terrible. / The journey was a nightmare.

UNIT 04

🌑 4.1
Part 1
M = Mike
M: Like a lot of people, I used to have a pretty fixed routine each day, and I often felt bored and frustrated. I used to dream of winning the lottery and having an exciting life. Then I came across an article that changed the way I think. It said, 'You don't need to do anything major to make life more interesting, just try a few simple changes'. The article went on to give some suggestions and here are a few examples:
- Take a different route to work or school
- Cook one new dish every week
- Have lunch with someone you don't know well at work or school
- Start a conversation with a stranger every day
- Find free activities to do in the evenings and at weekends
- Call a different friend or relative every week

◐ 4.2
Part 2
M = Mike, J = Jack, A = Amy

M: So, I started to make some of these changes. For example, I always used to complain that you need a lot of money to have fun. It's just not true. A quick search on the Internet or in my local paper, and I found lots of free activities – exhibitions at museums and galleries, walks to places of interest, concerts given by local schools and clubs. In a month I went out three or four times a week, and every weekend, and it didn't cost me a thing. I tried everything from an opera performed by the music society to a demonstration of judo at the sports club.
Then I decided to put all of these ideas on a website. I was amazed at the number of people who visited the site and left positive comments. But don't just take it from me. First, Amy:

A: When I think about it, I was really boring. I did the same things day after day. I used to drive to work and get stuck in the same traffic jam all the time. How silly is that? So, I started to take a different route and I noticed things I'd never seen before – a lovely old church, a beautiful line of trees for example. Now I walk or cycle whenever I can. I have to get up earlier but it's worth it because I'm in a much better mood when I get to work.

M: And also Jack:

J: I'm into sport and I'm quite good at it. But I found that even something I enjoy could become boring. I was definitely a creature of habit. I used to train on the same days, at exactly the same time, and do exactly the same things. All my friends were playing the same sports, so I never met anyone new. Then someone mentioned Mike's website and I decided to check it out. The advice there was beautifully simple – add variety and you will get your motivation back. Now I do a different exercise routine every day, have taken up judo for the first time, and I'm also helping local kids get into sport. I feel so much more positive.

M: So there you have it. Simple changes for a more interesting day. Why not give it a try? What have you got to lose?

◐ 4.3

1   Like a lot of people, I used to have a pretty fixed routine.
2   I'm in a much better mood when I get to work.
3   I'm into sport and I'm quite good at it.
4   All my friends were playing the same sports,
5   What have you got to lose?

Unit 05

◐ 5.1
Speaker 1

It was a friend's birthday the day before the interview, and he invited a group of us to go for a meal. I was going to go for an hour and then head home to prepare for the interview. Well, we were having such a good time that when I looked at my watch, I couldn't believe it was 11:30. I went home and straight to bed, promising myself I would get up early and look for some information about the company on the Internet. My alarm went off at 6:30 but I just ignored it and went back to sleep. I got to the interview in good time, but I wasn't feeling very confident because I hadn't had time to do any research on the company. Every time the interviewer asked me something, my mind just went blank.

Speaker 2

I didn't get on well with my boss and I'd been fed up in my job for a while. So I was really pleased when I saw a vacancy at a local advertising agency. I spent quite a lot of time finding out about the agency and thinking of questions to ask the interviewer. I booked the day off and I had my suit dry-cleaned. On the morning of the interview I was feeling quite confident. I left the house in plenty of time and got a bus but then we hit a traffic jam. We were stuck there for ages before I decided to walk. It was further than I thought, so when I arrived for the interview, another candidate had taken my place. I was so annoyed that I was a bit rude to the receptionist, which isn't really like me. Not a great start.

Speaker 3

Being interviewed is my idea of hell. I get *so* nervous that I can't think straight! I saw the job ad in the local paper and it sounded really good, so I decided to go for it. I thought I would prepare well and list all my skills and positive points. I was determined to make a good impression. I got into the interview room and my nerves took over. I didn't listen to the interviewers' questions, I just went on about how brilliant I am. Then one of them asked me, 'What are your weaknesses?' and I actually said, 'I don't have any. I think I am the candidate you are looking for.' They all looked at each other in surprise and then suddenly the interview was over. I can't believe I was so stupid.

Speaker 4

I'd done the same design job for quite a while so I was ready for a change. I quite liked working in the department, but my boss wasn't particularly creative. I spotted the vacancy on the staff noticeboard so I thought I'd apply. I didn't need to spend too long preparing as it was a similar job, just in a different department. I don't get too nervous in interviews and I knew how the organisation works, so I just had a few questions up my sleeve. Then the interviewer asked, 'So, why do you want to move departments?' Stupidly, I said that I didn't think my boss was much good at design and that I couldn't learn anything from her. The room went silent and the interviewers just stared at me. Needless to say, I didn't get that job and now I need to move company.

Speaker 5

I work in sales. I wasn't really looking to change jobs but then a friend sent me some information about a rep's job where she works. It was a role with more responsibility, so I thought, 'Why not?' She filled me in on what the company was like and helped me think about what to say on the day. I arrived on time and met the interviewers. It all seemed to be going OK, then I spotted some croissants on the desk and I remembered I'd skipped breakfast. So, I asked for a coffee and croissant. The head of sales looked a bit surprised but he handed them both over. I was enjoying my late breakfast when my mobile rang. I answered it because it was one of my co-workers. Then suddenly, the head of sales stopped the interview. He said he thought I was wasting their time, which was a bit odd.

5.2

1 ... he invited a group of us to go for a meal.
2 ... when I looked at my watch, I couldn't believe it was 11:30.
3 My alarm went off at 6:30 but I just ignored it and went back to sleep.
4 Every time the interviewer asked me something, my mind just went blank.
5 It sounded really good, so I decided to go for it.
6 ... I remembered I'd skipped breakfast.
7 The head of sales looked a bit surprised but handed them both over.
8 I answered it because it was one of my co-workers.

Unit 06

6.1
E = Emma, J = Jodie

E: Hi, Jodie, and welcome back. It's great to see you after such a long time.

J: Thanks, Emma. Good to see you, too. We had a wonderful time, but it's great to be home.

E: You were away for about six weeks, weren't you?

J: That's right – touring Malaysia, Singapore and Hong Kong. I've got tons of photos. You must come and see them when I've put them onto my laptop. In the meantime, I've got a few pressies for you.

E: Jodie, you haven't bought us presents, have you?

J: Of course. I like to bring things back for people. It's kind of a way of sharing the experience. So, this is for you. I thought the colours would suit you.

E: A silk scarf! It's beautiful. Thank you, you shouldn't have. Did you buy one for yourself?

J: No, but don't worry I did loads of shopping. I had to buy an extra suitcase for all my stuff. I got a fantastic silk shirt in Singapore. I wanted Nick to get a suit made by a local tailor but he didn't seem interested.

E: Men hate shopping for clothes, don't they?

J: Oh, I know. But Nick made up for it in Hong Kong with all the techno shops. He bought a new laptop and an iPod.

E: He didn't buy one of those amazing designer watches, did he?

J: No, but only because we ran out of money! Anyway, back to your presents. I wasn't sure what to bring for Eddie, so I went for Chinese herbs and spices, and some sauces. I know that he loves cooking.

E: Perfect, thank you.

J: Oh, and four sets of chopsticks to eat with. You know how to eat with chopsticks, don't you?

E: Well, Eddie and I do, but the kids have never tried, so that will be fun for them.

J: And not forgetting the kids. Flying kites is very popular in Asia, so I bought them each a kite. I hope that's OK.

E: That's great. They'll love going out with them on a windy day. Thanks so much, it's really kind of you.

J: Well, that's what friends are for, isn't it?

6.2
1 You were away for about six weeks, weren't you?
2 Jodie, you haven't bought us presents, have you?
3 Men hate shopping for clothes, don't they?
4 He didn't buy one of those amazing designer watches, did he?
5 You know how to eat with chopsticks, don't you?
6 Well, that's what friends are for, isn't it?

UNIT 07

7.1

P = Presenter, M1 = Man 1, W1 = Woman 1, TG = Teen girl, TB = Teen boy, M2 = Man 2, W2 = Woman 2

P: With news of record-breaking exam results but also problems with failing schools, we're here on the streets of London to ask: What makes a good school? Sir, can I ask you: What makes a good school?

M1: Well, I'm retired now but boarding school certainly worked for me. It taught me to be independent. There's too much talk of feelings and looking after pupils in school nowadays.

P: OK, thanks for that.
    ... Excuse me, madam, we're asking people what they think makes a good school.

W1: For me, it's discipline. I'm glad I went to school in Ghana because everyone paid attention in class and respected the teacher. Here, schools need more teachers who are good at controlling the class, because the kids think they know it all.

P: I'm sure many of our viewers will share that opinion, thank you.
    Ah a couple of teenagers ... can I ask you a very relevant question: What makes a good school?

TG: Sure. Well, I think it's all down to the teachers. Good teachers can be an inspiration to their class and encourage them to do wel ... And if they make the classes lively and interesting, then most of the students will pay attention.

P: How about you?

TB: Well, I don't actually go to school.

P: What do you mean? You skip classes every day?

TB: No, nothing like that. I'm home educated – er, my mum and dad are my tutors and I study at home.

P: That's very unusual. Do you mind if I ask why?

TB: No, it's fine. I went to the local school for two years but the teachers didn't push us much and I got bored. So, my mum and dad decided to teach me themselves. It's kind of cool. I can plan my own learning but I still have to take exams.

P: Interesting experiences there, thank you both.

TG: Sure.

TB: No problem.

P: Let's get another opinion. Sir, would you mind if I asked you a question about education: What makes a good school?

M2: Well, I went to a Montessori school in Holland.

P: A Montessori school? Can you explain what that means?

M2: Of course. Maria Montessori was an Italian woman who developed an approach to educate the whole child, rather than just giving information. The teachers see each child in the class as an individual and encourage learning in lots of different ways, inside and outside the classroom.

P: Sounds interesting. Thanks for that.
    ... Let's see what this lady thinks. Excuse me, can I ask you a question on education: what do you think makes a good school?

W2: I'm glad you asked me that – I'm a head teacher of a school here in London!

P: Well, you're the person to ask ...

W2: You could say that. Well, schools are only really as good as their students. If students have a positive attitude, then they will learn. Of course, the teacher can give encouragement and try to inspire the class, but if a child won't co-operate, then there's little we can do. Parents, too, need to support and motivate their children. There should be a partnership between the school, the child and the parents.

P: So, it's all about co-operation between teachers and families. Thank you for that. If you have any views on what you've just heard, contact our message board and have your say. Now it's back to the studio ...

7.2

1 Good teachers can be an inspiration to their class and encourage them to do well.

2 Sir, would you mind if I asked you a question about education?

3 Maria Montessori was an Italian woman who developed an approach to educate the whole child.

4 Of course, the teacher can give encouragement and try to inspire the class, but if a child won't co-operate, then there's little we can do.

5 So, it's all about co-operation between teachers and families.

UNIT 08

8.1

P = Presenter, A = Annie

P: Hello and welcome to 'Fifteen minutes to fabulous' ... the cookery show that tells you how to prepare a dish in just a quarter of an hour. Just because you're in a rush, it doesn't mean you have to live on ready meals. This is fast food, but home style.
    I'm Marcus Flint and our guest chef today is Annie Mitchell, with a quick dish that's suitable for all the family. Annie ...

A: Thanks, Marcus. Yes, today we have cheesy pasta with spinach.

P: Sounds good. So, what do we need and how many people will it feed?

A: OK. This is a dish for four people and here's what you need: 1 medium onion, peeled and chopped, 200 grams of spinach, washed and finely chopped, 450 grams of pasta, about 2 tablespoons extra virgin olive oil, a little butter, a handful of basil leaves, and about 100 grams of grated cheese.

P: Right, so what do we do first?

A: First thing is to get the pasta cooking, so we need a large saucepan of boiling salted water... .
    ... In with the pasta and that will take about 12 minutes to cook. Remember, don't overcook pasta or it will be soggy and horrible.
    Next, we heat the oil and butter in a frying pan over a medium heat and add the onions... .
    ... Fry gently for about five minutes until soft and golden. Now our spinach. Turn the heat down, ... and then ... add the spinach to the frying pan.

... Mix it gently with the onions until it cooks down – it takes only a couple of minutes.

P: So you don't need to boil or steam the spinach first? ...

A: No, if you do that, you lose some of the flavour and the lovely green colour. And if you cook it straight in the pan you don't lose any if the vitamins.

P: OK, right.

A: And finally drain the pasta really well – you don't want it to be watery. Add the pasta to the onion and spinach and mix well... .

... Finally, add in the cheese and the basil leaves and give one final stir... .

... And there you have it. Cheesy pasta with spinach ... . Come and try it, Marcus.

P: ... Mmm, that's really tasty. A great dish for vegetarians, too.

A: That's right. Of course you could change some of the ingredients, add a few olives and some garlic. And if you can't live without meat or fish, add a bit of chicken or maybe some prawns to the onions and fry gently. It's just so versatile.

P: Great to see you, Annie and thanks for your recipe, which you can find on the 'Fifteen minutes to fabulous' website.

8.2

ee   ah   oo   er   or

8.3

1 prawn   corn   portion   foreign
2 starving   overcharged   marinate   half
3 cheese   steam   rich   peanut
4 decor   turn   stir   deserted
5 tablespoon   soup   tough   food

UNIT 09

9.1
Part 1
W = William, P = Paul

W: Clarkson and Lylle, good morning.

P: Oh, hi there. I saw your ad for a flat on Oak Street.

W: Ah, yes, number 29. It's just come on the market. It's nice and compact and very conveniently located – only about ten minutes from the tube.

P: Sure, but I need to know how much the rent is. I'm on a tight budget.

W: Oh, very affordable, very affordable. So, the flat needs a bit of work, you know, a good clean and maybe a new coat of paint.

P: OK, but everything depends on the rent.

W: I understand. So, when would you like to see the flat?

P: Erm, I can make two o'clock today but can you tell me about the rent?

W: And the name is?

P: Paul, Paul Mitchell.

W: Splendid, Mr Mitchell. I'm William Lylle – that's L-Y-DOUBLE-L-E – and I shall see you at 29 Oak Street at two today.

P: Yes, OK, but I do need to know how much the rent is ...

9.2
Part 2
R = Rachel, P = Paul

R: So, any luck with the flat? What was it like?

P: It was a complete waste of time!

R: How come?

P: Well, you expect flats to be compact, but this was a joke. You couldn't call it compact, it was just cramped. The kitchen was about half the size of a cupboard.

R: Yes, but you have to start somewhere.

P: I know, but it wasn't just the size. There wasn't any central heating.

R: Mmm, a bit chilly then?

P: It wasn't chilly, it was freezing. And it's only April! What would it be like in winter?

R: Mmm, you're right. What about the location? Where is Oak Street?

P: Down by the park. It's quite a nice area but not very conveniently located. The agent said it was ten minutes from the tube, but it was more like twenty. And that's not all ... the state of the place. The agent said it needed 'a bit of work' but it was completely run down. The roof needed fixing and the bathroom and kitchen were really dirty.

R: So, how much was the rent on this place?

P: The agent didn't tell me until I'd actually seen it – £550 a month. It was supposed to be affordable but that's just overpriced. It's not worth it.

R: No wonder you're not going to take it.

P: Hmm. It's a shame because I wanted to live by myself but I think I'm going to have to try a shared flat.

9.3

1 You couldn't call it compact, it was just cramped.
2 It wasn't chilly, it was freezing.
3 The agent said it was ten minutes from the tube, but it was more like twenty.
4 It was supposed to be affordable, but that's just overpriced.

9.4

1 It's too far to walk to the shops, so you have to get the bus.
2 The flat isn't on the first floor, it's in the basement.
3 We didn't meet the landlord, just the other tenants.
4 We can't help you move on Friday but we'll come round at the weekend.
5 I expected the decor to be quite trendy but it was really old-fashioned.

UNIT 10

🔊 10.1
One
W = Woman, M = Man

W: We haven't been to the cinema for ages. Do you fancy going tonight?

M: Erm, not really. I checked earlier and there's nothing on.

W: Oh, well, how about something to eat? We could try that new steak house on the High Street.

M: Actually, I'd rather go at the weekend if that's OK with you. There's quite a good film on later tonight.

W: OK, another night in front of the TV then.

Two
B = Boy, M = Mum

B: Mum, the new *Batman* film starts this week. Tom from school is going to the nine o'clock showing tomorrow. Can I go too?

M: Not at nine o'clock on a school day. What other showings are there?

B: Erm, 4:30 and seven o'clock.

M: Well, there won't be time to make the 4:30 after school, so if you go tomorrow, it will have to be seven o'clock.

B: OK, I'll text Tom and ask him to go at seven, too.

Three
M = Man, W = Woman

M: I just love his work, don't you?

W: Oh, yes. It's the second time I've been to this exhibition. Apparently, he's really talented. He does photography and videos as well.

M: Really? That's interesting. But come and look at this landscape. The use of colour is amazing and his technique is really different.

W: I know. Wouldn't it be fantastic to have that hanging in your own front room?

Four
W = Woman, M = Man

W: So, did you enjoy it?

M: That was the best thing I've seen in ages.

W: It was good, wasn't it. I couldn't believe the ending.

M: The whole idea was so clever. It kept me guessing right to the end.

W: I know. And no silly special effects for a change – just an interesting story. The only problem for me was the soundtrack – a bit too loud.

Five
W = Woman, S = Son

W: It will be so nice to go in to London *together*. Shall we meet for a coffee near the station first?

S: I'd rather we didn't, Mum – that part of town is a bit rough nowadays.

W: Oh, dear. I didn't know that. What about in the main square? That always used to be quite posh.

S: Well, it's a bit far to walk to the station from there. Listen, I'll pick you up from home and we can have a coffee on the train.

Six
TB = Teen boy, TG = Teen girl

TB: You know where the ice rink is, don't you?

TG: Erm, is it down from the station?

TB: No, that was the old one. They closed it years ago. The new one is at the back of the shopping centre.

TG: Is it right opposite the Internet café?

TB: Yes, that's the one. I'll see you there at six.

🔊 10.2
1 Do you fancy going tonight? / Come and look at this landscape.
2 There's nothing on. / That always used to be quite posh.
3 What other showings are there? / That part of town is a bit rough nowadays.
4 He does videos as well. / No silly special effects for a change.
5 It's the second time I've been to this exhibition. / He does photography as well.
6 Is it right opposite the Internet cafe? / What about in the main square?

UNIT 11

🔊 11.1
1 sound effect of a bear
2 sound effect of a parrot
3 sound effect of a dolphin
4 sound effect of a wolf
5 sound effect of a crow
6 sound effect of a whale

🔊 11.2
M = Mark, A = Amy

M: You'll never guess what happened to me last weekend.

A: Go on. What?

M: I was thrown out of the local safari park.

A: Why? And what were you doing there anyway? You're not really an animal person.

M: No, I know, but ... I'd been promising to take a friend's son, Jake, to the safari park for ages and it was his birthday on Sunday. Everything started well – the weather was great and we arrived at the park at about 11. The first section had local animals – there were red deer and squirrels ... things like that. Then we moved on to the interesting stuff like lions and tigers. Well, by this time it had got really hot and the air conditioning in the car wasn't working, so I decided to open the sun roof – only a couple of inches.

A: But you're not supposed to do that, are you?

M: No, and the next thing I knew, there was a big angry warden in a jeep next to us shouting 'Close your sun roof!' So, I did and we moved on to the hippo lake.

A: So what happened next?

M: Well, it was so hot that all the hippos were under the water and we couldn't see anything. Jake wanted a drink but I'd left our picnic in the boot. So I just got out of the car for a second to get some water. Then, the same warden appeared out of nowhere shouting, 'Get back in your car immediately!' I didn't think that hippos were that dangerous.

A: Mark, everyone knows you're not allowed to get out of your car.

M: Yeah, but Jake needed a drink and there were no animals nearby. Anyway, we drove on for a bit to the monkey reserve. They're one of Jake's favourite animals so I stopped for him to have a good look. Then one of the baboons sat on the front of the car. It didn't break anything but we had to wait ages for it to move. So, I started the car and drove a bit faster than the speed limit. Jake thought it was so funny to be driving along with a baboon on the car and then …

A: Don't tell me – the warden!

M: Yeah. I was so shocked to see him that I had to brake quickly and the baboon slid off the car. It wasn't hurt or anything. Then I saw that the weight of the animal had left a big dent on the bonnet. I was so annoyed. I said I was going to write to the manager and complain but the warden said all visitors drive through the park at their own risk. That can't be right, can it?

A: I think it is. You should have read the rules … before you went in. So what happened in the end?

M: Well, I asked for my money back, they refused and then they asked me to leave the park. They said I was a bad example to other visitors.

A: Oh dear. Do you know whether you'll be allowed to go back?

M: To be honest, I'd rather not go again. I'll take Jake to the zoo next time!

🔊 11.3
M = Mark, A = Amy

1

M: I'd been promising to take a friend's son

M: I decided to open the sun roof

2

M: The weather was great

A: Do you know whether you'll be allowed to go back?

3

M: It didn't break anything

M: I had to brake quickly.

4

M: There were red deer and squirrels, things like that.

A: You should have read the rules.

5

M: I said I was going to write to the manager.

M: That can't be right, can it?

6

M: We had to wait ages for it to move.

M: The weight of the animal had left a big dent.

Unit 12

🔊 12.1
Part 1
P = Presenter

P: We all have contact with a wide range of people every day – family, friends, colleagues – but is friendship changing in the 21st century? According to research from the early 1990s, people have an average of 150 contacts in their social network. This includes about five close friends. But thanks to the Internet, some people claim to have hundreds or even thousands of 'friends' on social networking sites like *Facebook* and *MySpace*. These friends may even include famous people who join the sites. However, a recent survey has shown that the actual number of true online friends is just five. So, it seems that maintaining friendships in cyberspace is similar to real life.

🔊 12.2
Part 2
P = Presenter, N = Natalie, W = William, A = Adrian, T = Trisha

P: So, we asked a few people about their network of friends. Here's what they had to say …

N: My name's Natalie and I'm 17. I'm really into *Facebook* and *MySpace* and I have hundreds of friends all over the world. People say that they aren't *real* friends, but I don't agree. I went to visit two of them in New York last year and they are coming here to visit me. So, I made new friends I would never have met without the Internet. Of course, I have friends at college that I meet up with every day.

W: I'm William and in my fifties. I'm a company director so I have a lot of colleagues and a big circle of acquaintances – you know – people I see once in a while for business, or people I say hello to on the train or at the golf club. In terms of close friends, there are two guys I went to school with. We keep in touch as much as possible, but I don't see them very often. Of course, my best friend is my wife.

A: My name's Adrian and I'm just 24. Friends? Well, I'm a bit of a loner, so my circle of friends is quite small. If you ask me, it's better to have two or three friends you can trust than to be in a big group. I'm not much of a computer person so I never go on *Facebook* or *MySpace*. I use emails to stay in touch with family and close friends but I'd rather see people face to face than sit at a computer.

T: I'm Trisha and I'm in my mid-40s. I'm a mature student, doing a degree in graphic design. I'm quite outgoing and chatty so I have quite a big circle of friends. A group of about 12 schoolfriends and I meet up once a month for a drink. I've also made a lot of new friends on my course. I'm into social networking, too, and I must have a few hundred cyber friends in different parts of the world. It all makes life a bit more fun!

⊘ 12.3

1 I have hundreds of friends all over the world.
2 I have friends at college that I meet up with every day.
3 I have a lot of colleagues and a big circle of acquaintances.
4 We keep in touch as much as possible.
5 Well, I'm a bit of a loner.
6 My circle of friends is quite small.
7 I'm quite outgoing and chatty.
8 I've also made a lot of new friends on my course.

UNIT 13

⊘ 13.1
P = Presenter

P: Welcome back to *Lifelines*, the programme that tries to make everyday life just a bit more manageable. Today, we have with us Penny Marshall, professional life coach in the business sector. She's joined us to talk about commuting and how to survive it. Penny, nice to have you on the show. So, how long do people spend commuting each day?

⊘ 13.2
P = Presenter, B = Penny

P: Welcome back to *Lifelines*, the programme that tries to make everyday life just a bit more manageable. Today, we have with us Penny Marshall, professional life coach in the business sector. She's joined us to talk about commuting and how to survive it. Penny, nice to have you on the show. So, how long do people spend commuting each day?

B: Well, people in the UK spend an average of 45 minutes travelling to and from work. That's longer than in other European countries and works out at about 139 hours a year or 19 working days. Of course, transport problems like train delays and cancellations, or traffic jams, can make your commute considerably longer.

P: So, what can people do?

B: Well, of course people use different forms of transport to get to work, so let's start with travellers by train. It sounds simple, but if your usual train is always packed, why not try an earlier or later one? Many bosses are flexible about hours, provided they know when to expect you. Setting off half an hour earlier or later might mean you get a seat in a quieter carriage. It's worth a try.

P: But what about if all the morning trains are full or if there is a delay?

B: Sure, and this is the reality for hundreds of people every day. My advice is to plan your journey. Take something to do, preferably something you enjoy rather than work. So, reading a book or magazine, doing a puzzle, or writing a letter to a friend. Or why not try something creative? Several of my clients take knitting on the train. Try anything that keeps your mind off the journey and has some positive result.

P: Good advice. But what if you can't get a seat? A lot of commuters have to stand on the train.

B: Of course, you're right. And that can be very uncomfortable. People don't like losing their personal space and can get very stressed. In these cases, try accepting the situation and relaxing your mind. Focus on your breathing and think of something nice – a place that you love, a happy experience or a funny conversation. And try not to talk to other commuters for too long.

P: That's surprising. Why is that?

B: Well, it's OK to chat for a few minutes, but talking for a long time can be tiring. And if you are in a group of stressed people who are all complaining about the trains, you will end up in a really bad mood yourself.

P: Yes, I see. That makes sense.

B: One other tip is to try a bit of exercise. Not aerobics of course, but if you tense and then relax every muscle in your body from your head to your toes, it can get rid of stress. Car drivers can try that, too.

P: Thanks for that, Penny. Stay tuned and we'll be back in a second with more interesting advice for commuters. But first, here's …

⊘ 13.3

1 you get a seat in a quieter carriage
2 preferably something you enjoy rather than work
3 Several of my clients take knitting on the train
4 that can be very uncomfortable
5 more interesting advice for commuters

UNIT 14

⊘ 14.1
Part 1
R = Richard, S = Sat nav

R: Right, I've set up the sat nav. I think I've got everything I need for my presentation. There's plenty of time before my interview, so off we go.

S: At the end of the road, turn right.

R: OK, turning right.

S: Cross the roundabout, second exit. Then take the first right.

R: OK, round the roundabout, second exit.

S: Take the first right… . Take the first right.

R: What? Stupid machine. I can't take the first right. It's pedestrianised.

S: Off route … recalculating.

R: Why didn't you know that I couldn't drive down that road? You're supposed to make my life easier!

S: Take the third right.

R: OK, third road on the right... . Oh, I don't believe it. A huge traffic jam. And I've only got 40 minutes before my interview.

Part 2
R = Richard, A = Receptionist, C = Clive Marshall

R: Good morning, my name's Richard Blake. I'm being interviewed this morning and I need to set up my stuff to give a presentation.

A: Yes, you're in room 211. All the equipment should be in there. I'll ask someone from IT to pop over to check everything is OK.

R: Great thanks... . OK... . Here we are. I've plugged in my laptop – that seems fine. Just need to check the microphone. Testing, testing, 1, 2, 3... . Oh, hell, the mike doesn't work. It's such a big room, they'll never hear me.

C: Good morning, Richard Blake?

R: Oh, great, you're here. Now, I need a new microphone as this thing doesn't work. Have you got one with you? I'm very short of time – I'm being interviewed in 10 minutes.

C: Yes, Mr Blake, I know. I'm not from IT. I'm Clive Marshall, MD of this company.

R: Oh, I'm so sorry. The receptionist said someone from IT would be here and I just assumed ...

C: Yes, I see. Let me ring IT for you.

R: Thanks, thank you Mr Marshall, that's very good of you. Sorry.

Part 3
R = Richard, C = Clive Marshall

R: OK, starting with my analysis of the current market. As you can see, the market for organic food has risen steadily in the last five years... . And if we break this down further, we can see that fruit and vegetables are growing steadily but the biggest change can be seen in this graphic ...

C: Mr Blake. There seems to be a problem with the images on the screen. There are photos of a young child on the beach, not developments in market share for organic food.

R: No, I don't believe it. I must have picked up the wrong CD from home. I've got the one for my daughter's holiday project. I'm so sorry. Could we reschedule the presentation for later this week? I have some very interesting ideas ...

C: I think we'll leave it there, actually, Mr Blake. We have a number of other people to see.

14.2

1 Yes, you're in room 211. / That's very good of you.

2 I've got everything I need for my presentation. / The market for organic food has risen steadily.

3 At the end of the road, turn right. / Take the third right.

4 You're supposed to make my life easier! / I've plugged in my laptop.

5 Starting with my analysis of the current market. / Now I need a new microphone.

6 There seems to be a problem with the images on the screen. / There are photos of a young child on the beach.

UNIT 15

15.1
One
M = Man, W = Woman

M: Oh, Sue. Are you OK? Let me help you up.

W: Thanks ... Ow!

M: Careful. Have you hurt your wrist?

W: No, I don't think so. Ouch!

M: Put your arm round my shoulder. Can you stand?

W: Yes, but I can't put any weight on it. I think I might have broken my ankle.

M: Sit down. I'll get Mike to take you to the hospital.

Two
P = Patient, D = Doctor

P: I think I need some antibiotics, doctor.

D: Why, what seems to be the problem?

P: I can't stop coughing. I was up most of last night.

D: Have you had a high temperature at all?

P: No, but my head really hurts.

D: I can't really give you antibiotics unless you have some sort of infection. Just rest, take some painkillers and plenty of fluids. I'm sure you'll be fine in a couple of days.

Three
G = Girl, D = Dad

G: I'm just preparing the vegetables for dinner ... Ow!

D: What have you done?

G: I've cut myself really badly.

D: Let me have a look.

G: I think I'll need some stitches.

D: Emma, don't be such a baby. It's a tiny cut. Just wash it under the tap.

G: Can I have a bandage?

D: You don't need a bandage. I'll just get you some cream.

G: OK, but can you finish the dinner? I feel a bit dizzy. I think I need to lie down.

Four

M = Man, W = Woman

M: You know I've been under the weather recently?

W: Yes, you said you were getting a nasty rash and that you were sneezing a lot.

M: Well, I got the doctor to check me out and he sent me for some tests. It turns out I have an allergy.

W: Don't tell me you're allergic to milk, or wheat, or nuts. There's this woman at work who eats hardly anything. I'm sure it's all in her imagination.

M: No, nothing like that. I can still eat fish, cheese and prawns – in fact, all my favourite foods.

W: So what's up then? Why do you keep getting a rash?

M: It turns out I've developed an allergy to cats and dogs.

W: *[Laughs]* You're kidding. But you're a vet. You're supposed to love animals.

M: I DO love animals… . It's not funny!

W: No, I know, sorry. It's just so weird. I bet you would prefer a food allergy, wouldn't you? It must be very difficult …

15.2

1 I can't stop coughing.
2 Let me have a look.
3 It's a tiny cut.
4 You don't need a bandage.
5 He sent me for some tests.
6 It turns out I have an allergy.
7 Why do you keep getting a rash?

15.3

1 dizzy   antibiotics   stiff   itchy
2 bump   cut   blood   pressure
3 stomach   bandage   rash   allergy
4 cough   doctor   swollen   got
5 medicine   headache   feel   infection
6 arthritis   temperature   broken   medication
7 should   shoulder   good   pulled

UNIT 16

16.1

A = Announcer

A: It has been confirmed that a collision with a flock of birds caused US Airways Flight 1549 to crash-land on the Hudson River in New York on January the 15th, 2009. All 155 passengers and crew survived the landing on the water, which made headlines round the world.

16.2

A = Announcer

A: It has been confirmed that a collision with a flock of birds caused US Airways Flight 1549 to crash-land on the Hudson River in New York on January the 15th, 2009. All 155 passengers and crew survived the landing on the water, which made headlines round the world.

The flight left New York's LaGuardia Airport at 15:26 local time headed for Charlotte in North Carolina. It was in the air for less than three minutes before the pilot, Captain Chesley B Sullenberger, reported the collision with the birds and the loss of power to both engines of the aircraft. The plane had only managed to reach a top altitude of 3 200 feet (about 975 metres).

At about 15:30 Captain Sullenberger took the decision to land the plane on the water that divides Manhattan from New Jersey. Apart from one person who had broken legs, none of the people on board suffered serious injuries. The passengers and crew were safely evacuated from the plane and picked up by commercial ferries and water rescue vehicles. Captain Sullenberger was the last person to leave the aircraft.

The crew, and particularly Captain Sullenberger, were described as heroes for their actions by both the governor and mayor of New York. Former US president George Bush praised the pilot for his 'amazing skills in bringing his plane down safely, for his bravery, and for his heroic efforts to ensure the safety of his passengers and the people in the area'.

Although this event may sound like just a freakish accident, birds represent an ongoing problem for the aviation industry. A spokesman from the US Federal Aviation Administration said, 'Aircraft are being struck every day by birds – the reason you don't hear so much about them is they are designed to take these impacts … But once you get to large flocks or large birds striking at a critical moment, that's where these events hit the news.'

It is thought that the loss of power to both engines on Flight 1549 was caused by hitting a flock of Canada geese, which can weigh from 1.5–5.5 kilos each. Overall, the FAA received almost 76 000 reports of bird strikes between 1990 and 2007. Statistics show that 219 people have died since 1988 in incidents involving animals colliding with planes and the overall cost of damage to aircraft in the US is estimated at 600 million dollars.

16.3

1 flight one five four nine
2 one hundred and fifty-five passengers
3 three thousand two hundred feet
4 nine hundred and seventy-five metres
5 five point five kilos
6 seventy-six thousand reports
7 since nineteen eighty-eight
8 six hundred million dollars

ANSWER KEY

UNIT 1

Grammar Question formation

A

1 What's your name?
2 Where are you from?
3 What do you do?
4 What do you do when you're not working?
5 How long have you studied English?
6 Why are you learning English?
7 Have you studied here before?
8 Have you met the teacher yet?
9 What do you think of the test we did?
10 What are you going to do after this class?

B

a 10   c 7   e 9   g 5   i 8
b 2   d 4   f 3   h 1   j 6

C

1 does a typical class involve
2 are there in a class
3 do they come from
4 does each class last
5 do you decide on a student's level
6 do the teachers have
7 are you going to use in the next course
8 does the course cost

D

1 *Which* language *uses* the Cyrillic alphabet?
   Russian
2 How *many* living languages *exist* in the world today?
   about 6,000
3 *How* do you *write* Hebrew and Arabic?
   from right to left
4 *Where* does the word 'alphabet' originally *come* from?
   the first two letters of the Greek alphabet
5 *What* percentage of the Internet *is* in English?
   56%
6 *Who created* the first computer programming language?
   a German engineer

Developing conversations Asking follow-up questions

A

1 Whereabouts?
2 How long have you been learning it?
3 What are you studying?
4 What year are you in?

B

1 What did you do?
2 Did you get anything nice?
3 How many brothers and sisters have you got?
4 Older or younger?

C

1 Where are you doing that?
2 So why are you studying English?
3 Where do you work?
4 What kind of music are you into?

Vocabulary Learning languages

A

1 my level is very basic   to speak slowly

2 teach myself
3 get by
4 fairly fluent   picked it up
5 maintain conversations on a range of topics
6 I am more or less bilingual

Vocabulary Language words

A

1 phrasal verb   6 verb
2 preposition   7 pronoun
3 adjective   8 adjective
4 adverb   9 verb
5 noun

B

1 hard
   fast
   not very fluent
   a serious mistake
   slow progress
   a high level of Japanese
2 make
   a mistake   progress
   a fool of yourself an effort
   do
   a course   a good job
   an exercise   your homework
3 worry about your progress
   concentrate on work
   rely on your best friend
   deal with a problem
4 e<u>v</u>idence   moti<u>v</u>ation
   en<u>v</u>ironment
   bilin<u>g</u>ual   contin<u>u</u>ity
   emb<u>a</u>rrassed
5 They all contain silent letters.
   honest   **w**rite
   kno**w**ledge   forei**g**n

Listening

A

1 c   2 a   3 c   4 b   5 a

Pronunciation Silent letters

A

1 I've signed up for a <u>b</u>uilding <u>c</u>ourse
2 an evening <u>c</u>ourse in a foreign language or <u>k</u>nitting or <u>w</u>hatever
3 there's a need for <u>b</u>uilders and plum<u>b</u>ers
4 the first class was a bit nerve-<u>w</u>racking
5 I felt such a fool and I went brigh<u>t</u> red

Reading

A

b Where's the strangest place you've had a language class?

B

1 Mike   5 Alex
2 Alex   6 Cerys
3 Cerys   7 Mike
4 Lydia

C

1 top up   4 get me out of a hole
2 rubbish   5 at ease
3 go a long way 6 wondered how on earth

GRAMMAR Narrative tenses

A

1 The German class started. I arrived.
When I arrived, the German class had already started.
2 I didn't recognise her. We met a few times before. Although we had met a few times before, I didn't recognise her.
3 She went bright red. She used the wrong word.
After she had used the wrong word, she went bright red.
4 Mike was late for the class. He left his books at home.
Mike was late for the class because he had left his books at home.
5 Ana spent an hour in the advanced class. She realised she was in the wrong room.
Ana had spent an hour in the advanced class before she realised she was in the wrong room.
6 I realised he was the boss. I asked him to make me a coffee.
I had asked him to make me a coffee before I realised he was the boss.

B

1 had just had
2 said
3 had already passed
4 was saving up
5 hadn't slept
6 felt
7 had arrived
8 were driving
9 saw
10 was moving
11 grabbed
12 had just done
13 drove
14 didn't say
15 was concentrating

GRAMMAR Other uses of the past continuous

A

1 h   3 g   5 e   7 a
2 b   4 f   6 d   8 c

DEVELOPING CONVERSATIONS John was telling me ...

A

1 No, I have private lessons. My tutor is really good – very patient.   4
Is he? So, what style do you play?   5
Yeah, that's right.   2
Amy was telling me you've taken up the guitar.   1
Classical. I like listening to rock but don't think I'm a Jimi Hendrix type!   6
Great! Are you teaching yourself to play?   3
2 Well, if I hear of anything, I'll let you know.   9
No, but I've only just started looking.   8
Yes, that's right.   2
Like a waiter or something?   5
Yes.   6
Have you had any luck yet?   7
Paul was telling me you're looking for a part-time job.   1
Well, maybe restaurant or bar work.   4
What sort of job are you looking for?   3
3 How long will you be away for?   5
Yes, news travels fast!   2
Well, good luck, I hope it goes well.   7
About twelve months, I think.   6
Katrina was telling me you're going to Argentina.   1
I've got a job in a language school.   4
That's amazing. What are you going to do?   3

DEVELOPING WRITING An anecdote

A

1 was studying
2 took
3 have
6 was
7 Before
8 had

4 While
5 did
9 checked
10 had chosen

B

Student's own answers.

VOCABULARY BUILDER QUIZ 1

A

a *slight* accent

B

1 e   2 d   3 b   4 c   5 a

C

1 top   2 spare   3 skills

D

1 Remind
2 reply
3 reconsider / rethink / revoke
4 reveal
5 rely

E

1 running
2 improve
3 keep
4 remind
5 involves

F

1 improvement
2 fluency
3 management
4 motivation
5 chatty
6 availability

UNIT 2

VOCABULARY Feelings

A

1 guilty
2 exhausted
3 confused
4 relaxed
5 annoyed
6 disappointed
7 pleased

B

1 terrible   stressed
2 upset   worried
3 in such a bad mood   furious
4 down   fed up

GRAMMAR Be, look, seem, etc

1 sounded really fed up
feel guilty
be upset
2 seem a bit down
was really pleased
felt embarrassed
3 looked a bit annoyed
felt disappointed
sound a lot more relaxed

DEVELOPING CONVERSATIONS Response expressions

A

1 d   2 a   3 f   4 b   5 c   6 e

LISTENING

A

b

B

1 F   3 T   5 T   7 T
2 F   4 F   6 T   8 T

Pronunciation

A

1 I'm not <u>normally</u> a <u>nervous</u> <u>person</u>, so I <u>felt</u> <u>pretty</u> <u>relaxed</u> about the <u>whole</u> <u>thing</u>.
2 I was wearing <u>jeans</u> and a <u>shirt</u>, but the <u>restaurant</u> was a <u>really</u> <u>elegant</u> <u>place</u>.
3 I was <u>really</u> <u>fed</u> <u>up</u> with <u>Annie</u> that she hadn't <u>warned</u> me it was a <u>formal</u> <u>dinner</u>.
4 To be <u>honest</u>, we hadn't been very <u>keen</u> on <u>most</u> of her <u>boyfriends</u>, so my <u>husband</u> and I were <u>rather</u> <u>worried</u> about the <u>dinner</u>.

Vocabulary Adjective collocations

A

1 relaxing friend / food
2 annoying disaster / success
3 disappointing problem / clothes
4 confusing idea / skill
5 exciting sleep / help
6 inspiring crime / loss

Grammar -ing / -ed adjectives

A

1 relaxed	annoying
2 embarrassing	shocked
3 confused	exhausting
4 surprised	annoying
5 interested	disappointing

B

a a gym   2
b a trip   4
c a health spa   1
d a novel   5
e a language school   3

C

1 A: interesting
   B: depressing
2 A: disappointed
   B: excited
3 A: amazing
   B: exhausted
4 A: embarrassed
   B: annoying

Reading

A
b

B

1 b   2 a   3 f   4 d   5 c   6 e

C

1 mood swings, 26% in panic attacks and anxiety, and 24% in depression.
2 Supporters included water, vegetables, fruit and oil-rich fish.
3 Stressors included sugar, caffeine, alcohol and chocolate.
4 and you must have enough fluid to prevent dehydration.

D

1 immediate	4 marked
2 right	5 directly
3 overall	6 regular

E

1 direct link
2 immediate effect
3 marked improvement
4 right foods
5 positive effect
6 improved mental health
7 regular physical exercise

Grammar Present continuous

1 A: are you wearing
   B: it looks
   A: we're meeting
2 A: are you doing
   B: I'm going   sounds
   A: I visit
3 A: are you being
   B: I'm working   We're giving   I'm still preparing
4 B: I always feel
   A: normally go   are doing

Grammar Present continuous / present simple questions

1 going   winning
2 are doing; Do fancy
3 are crying; Do want
4 are moving; is
5 are standing; Do need
6 Is enjoying; does do
7 do get; does take

Developing conversations Making excuses

A

1 I'd love to but I can't. I'm going away for the weekend.
2 B: I'm sorry, I can't. I'm working late this evening.
3 I'm afraid you can't. I don't have it with me.
4 It's nice of you to ask me. But I play in a band every Friday.
5 It's kind of you to ask us. But we go to London every weekend.
6 No, I'm sorry. I'm going out this evening.

Developing writing A letter – giving news

A

| 1 Sorry | 3 settling | 5 down | 7 miss | 9 hug |
| 2 pretty | 4 expect | 6 out | 8 into | 10 mind |

B

Student's own answers.

Vocabulary Builder Quiz 2

A

1 have a love-hate relationship
2 live in student accommodation
3 make a scientific discovery
4 give an inspiring speech
5 run a military campaign

B

1 line   2 hardly   3 stuck

C

2 Do you think you'll get promoted ~~up~~ next year?
5 When does Marcus graduate ~~up~~ from medical school?
6 Remember to protect ~~up~~ your skin in the sun.

D
1 mood   3 fed up   5 due
2 approach   4 attempt   6 loss

E
1 promoted
2 boredom
3 disappointed
4 meaningful
5 pleasure

UNIT 3

VOCABULARY Places of interest

A
1 palace   6 ruins   11 lake
2 galleries   7 theme park   12 by
3 old town   8 about ... outside 13 square
4 Out   9 outside   14 market
5 mosque / castle 10 castle / mosque 15 along

DEVELOPING CONVERSATIONS Recommendations

A
1 g   2 e   3 b   4 c   5 f   6 d

DEVELOPING WRITING An email – giving advice

A
suggestions of other things to do   4
ending   6
reason for writing   2
practical advice   5
greeting   1
where to go first   3

B
1 quick   3 take   5 straight 7 Anyway
2 during   4 at   6 down   8 time

C
1 time off   3 like   5 every day
2 ride   4 funny   6 for eating

D
1 b   2 g   3 e   4 a
5 f   6 h   7 d   8 c

E
Student's own answers.

VOCABULARY Holiday problems

A
1 delayed   stuck
2 arguing
3 with   windy
4 off
5 place   angry
6 crowded
7 up

B
1 B: had upset stomach; spoiled trip
2 A: missed flight; charged a fortune
3 B: stole passport; lost camera

LISTENING

A
a 2   b 4   c 5   d 3   e 1

PRONUNICIATION Same sound or different?

A
1 S   2 D   3 D   4 S   5 D   6 S

GRAMMAR Present perfect questions

A
1 A: Have   seen
  B:. I'd love to
2 A: Have   been
  B: never
3 A: Have   tried
  B: several times
4 A: Have   eaten
  B: to be
5 A: Have   ridden
  B: Have you?
6 A: Have   visited
  B: it
7 A: Have   flown
  B: is
8 A: Have   been
  B: go

READING

A
1 e   2 d   3 b   4 g   5 c   6 a

B
1 like the back of their hand
2 It's entirely up to
3 outstay your welcome
4 a bit awkward
5 a good track record
6 treat them to a meal

VOCABULARY Weather

A
freezing cold   a bit chilly   quite warm   hot   boiling hot

B
1 B: pour down
  B: keep out of
2 B: wet   clear up
3 A: heat
  B: reached
  A: humid
4 A: drop

GRAMMAR The future

A
1 We're going to be away in June.
2 I might try couch-surfing this year.
3 I've got to revise for my exams.
4 Jim is thinking of going travelling this summer.
5 It will probably be too cold for swimming.
6 They definitely aren't going on holiday in July.

B
1 I've got to study for my university entrance exam.
2 my friends and I are thinking of going camping near the coast
3 Marek and I are going to a concert in Manchester on Friday
4 I might be meeting up with some friends in London
5 I've got a free weekend
6 My sister and I aren't going to be around
7 I'll probably go to my friend's barbecue

C

1 A: are you going
  B: might   I've got
  A: got
  B: it'll
2 A: I'm having
  B: I'm going
  B: it'll probably take
3 A: We're going
  B: going   I'm spending
  B: of emigrating

VOCABULARY BUILDER QUIZ 3

A

1 charge	3 drop	5 debate
2 damage	4 link	6 mine

B

1 reopen	3 rejected	5 retook	7 rewind
2 repair	4 rearrange	6 redo	

C

1 d	2 b	3 e	4 f	5 a	6 c

D

1 P	2 N	3 N	4 P	5 N	6 P

UNIT 4

VOCABULARY Evening and weekend activities

A

play + on the computer, football, golf, tennis
go to + the gym, the cinema, a bar to watch the sport, a friend's house for dinner
go + cycling, clubbing, shopping, rollerblading, walking in the country
go for + a meal, a ride on my bike, a swim, a run

B

1 B: Well, go and play football or ride your bike.
  B: Well, stay in and tidy up your bedroom, then.
2 B: I just stayed in and took it easy.
  B: Yeah, I just didn't fancy going clubbing.
3 B: Going to a friend's for dinner or just taking it easy at home. What about you?
  A: My idea of heaven is staying in and studying for my exams.
  A: Only joking. My ideal night out is going to a bar to watch the football and then going clubbing.

GRAMMAR Frequency (present and past)

A

play golf   go walking in the country   eat out
go clubbing   go to the gym   work
1 A: How often do you eat out?
2 A: Do you ever work weekends?
3 A: Do you go to the gym much?
4 A: Do you ever play golf?
5 A: Do you go clubbing a lot?
6 A: How often do you go walking in the country?

B

5 a Not that
1 b All the
7 c ever
6 d used to
8 e Never

3 f often
4 g would
2 h every

C

1 used to have	4 used to leave
2 used to take	5 used to spend
3 not possible	

LISTENING

A

travel ✓
sport
food ✓
relationships ✓
free time ✓
shopping

B

Changing my morning routine has changed my attitude.   A
I became bored with my hobby even though I'm quite good at it.   J
I thought you needed money to have a good time.   M
It's silly to keep repeating things that upset you.   A
I wanted to share my ideas with other people.   M
I feel motivated to help others join in.   J
I developed a great social life at no cost.   M

PRONUNCIATION Sentence stress

A

1 <u>Like</u> a <u>lot</u> of <u>people</u>, I <u>used</u> to have a pretty <u>fixed</u> <u>routine</u>.
2 I'm in a <u>much</u> better <u>mood</u> when I <u>get</u> to <u>work</u>.
3 I'm into <u>sport</u> and I'm <u>quite</u> <u>good</u> at it.
4 <u>All</u> my <u>friends</u> were <u>playing</u> the <u>same</u> <u>sports</u>.
5 <u>What</u> have you <u>got</u> to <u>lose</u>?

DEVELOPING CONVERSATIONS Are you any good?

A

1 No, I'm useless.
2 Yeah, quite good.
3 I'm OK.
4 No, not really.

VOCABULARY Problems and sports

A

1 stiff
2 pulled
3 fell   broke
4 bloody
5 banged
6 beat
7 unfit

GRAMMAR Duration

A

1 How long did you train before the marathon?   d
2 How long has Jodie been doing ballet?   e
3 How long were you in plaster after your accident?   b
4 How long was your team in the first division?   a
5 How long have you been doing yoga?   c

B

1 A: I've been having riding lessons
  B: since then
2 A: How long have you been playing?
  B: for an hour

3 B: How long did you do that for?
    A: From the age of about 14 until I left.
4 B: Thanks. Until quite recently,
    A: That's amazing. How long did you teach for?

DEVELOPING WRITING An email asking for information

A

a It's the first time Richard has written to the organisation.
b He has never been part of a conservation group before.
e He asks about equipment.
f He says how he found out about the group.

B

1	advert	2	keen
3	experience	4	join
5	provided	6	confirm
7	grateful	8	let
9	forward	10	regards

C

Could you tell me whether any experience or special skills are necessary to join the group?
I would also like to know whether volunteers need to bring their own tools, or whether these will be provided .
Could you confirm the days and times that the group meets?
I would also be grateful if you could let me know whereabouts the group works and the type of tasks the volunteers do.
Finally, could you tell me if you organise any specialcourses in conservation?

D

1 Can you confirm if I have to wear anything special?
2 I would like to know how transport to each session is organised.
3 Can you confirm where the nearest car park to the gym is?
4 Could you tell me if the tutor has a good success rate?
5 I'd be grateful if you could tell me how much a course of lessons costs.
6 I would like to know if I have to take an exam or a test.

E

Student's own answers.

DEVELOPING CONVERSATIONS Music, films and books

A

1	much	3	All	5	in	7 anything
2	kind	4	mainly	6	stuff	

VOCABULARY Music

A

1	depressing	uplifting
2	bland	commercial
3	moving	sentimental
4	catchy	repetitive
5	heavy	soft

READING

A

b to give some facts about the problem of illegal downloads

B

2 the extent of the problem
4 possible solutions for the future
3 examples of people who have been punished
1 the ways people get music

C

1 'one or two': CDs
2 'This': file-sharing
3 'it': file-sharing
4 'this': music piracy
5 'one of them': organisations
6 'They': UK Internet providers and the record industry
7 'another possibility': to stop illegal downloaders
8 '80 per cent of them': 80% of downloaders

D

£1 billion cost of illegal downloading
14–24 age range
10,000 songs
48 per cent music collection
$222,000 fine given to Jamie Thomas
1, 702 number of songs Jamie Thomas had downloaded and distributed

E

1 A recent survey   The research also showed
2 The average
3 Nowadays
4 It is estimated

VOCABULARY BUILDER QUIZ 4

A

1	weights	3	warm-up	5	course
2	fit	4	season		

B

1 unfit
2 unlikely
3 unfair
4 unexpected
5 unreliable
6 uninspiring / uninteresting
7 unsuccessful
8 undecided

C

1	d	2	a	3	e	4	f	5	b	6 c

D

1	defence	3	training	5	injury
2	fitness	4	challenging	6	slippery

UNIT 5

VOCABULARY Jobs

A

1 civil servant
2 planner
   labourer
   electrician
3 programmer
   engineer
4 lawyer
   accountant
5 graphic designer
6 surgeon
7 estate agent
   security guard

B

civil servant	programmer
planner	engineer
labourer	lawyer
electrician	accountant

graphic designer
surgeon
estate agent
security guard

C

1 e   2 b   3 c   4 g   5 d   6 f   7 a

D

1 stressful   rewarding   surgeon
2 insecure   physically demanding   labourer
3 creative   varied   graphic designer
4 well paid   competitive   accountant
5 responsibility   paperwork   lawyer

VOCABULARY Work places and activities

A

1 I'm in sales. I'm the rep *for* the north-west.
2 I'm the warehouse manager. I prepare the orders for delivery and all the admin.
3 I work in the accounts department. I'm responsible for all the staff salaries.
4 I work in human res*ources*. I'm involved *in* recruitment.
5 I *am* part of the marketing team. I'm responsible *for* a big campaign for our new mobile phones.

B

1 representative, human resources, advertisement
2 curriculum vitae, Managing Director
3 public relations, personal assistant, administration
4 research and development, information technology

DEVELOPING CONVERSATIONS That must be …

A

1 That must be stressful.
2 That must be rewarding.
3 That must be disappointing.
4 That must be tiring.
5 That must be fascinating.
6 That must be fun.

LISTENING

A

a 5   b 4   c 3   d 2   e 1

PRONUNCIATION Past simple *-ed* endings

A

1 3   3 2   5 2   7 1
2 1   4 1   6 3   8 2

B

1 He invited a group of us to go for a meal.
2 When I looked at my watch, I couldn't believe it was 11.30.
3 My alarm went off at 6.30 but I just ignored it and went back to sleep.
4 Every time the interviewer asked me something, my mind just went blank.
5 It sounded really good, so I decided to go for it.
6 I remembered I'd skipped breakfast.
7 The head of sales looked a bit surprised but handed them both over.
8 I answered it because it was one of my co-workers.

GRAMMAR Have to, don't have to, can

A

1 We have to work a minimum of 35 hours a week.
2 You have to give more notice to book time off.
3 I have to put my staff under pressure to meet deadlines.
4 We can work from home at least one day a week.
5 Managers don't have to wear a suit unless they are meeting clients.
6 The staff can take 25 days' holiday a year.
7 The security guard doesn't have to check people's bags.

B

1 What time do you have to get up for work?
2 Can we work flexi-time?
3 How many hours does Rob have to work?
4 Can Lisa work from home?
5 How much do the reps have to travel every year?
6 Can the staff use computers to send personal emails?
7 Do you have to work weekends?

C

1 have to   4 can't   7 have to   10 didn't have to
2 could   5 had to   8 don't have
3 couldn't   6 could   9 has to

GRAMMAR Talking about rules

A

1 are not allowed to drink
2 are allowed to buy
3 are supposed to clear
4 shouldn't really send
5 are not supposed to leave
6 should really turn off

B

1 You are not allowed *to* die in the Houses of Parliament in London.
2 You are not suppose*d* to put a stamp showing the British king or queen's head upside-down on an envelope.
3 In Scotland, if someone knocks on your door and asks to use your toilet, you have *to* let them come in.
4 In Ohio, you *are not* allowed to get a fish drunk.
5 In Florida, unmarried women *are not* supposed to parachute on a Sunday.
6 In Vermont, a woman has to get written permission from her husband to wear false teeth.
7 In Milan, you have *to* smile at all times, except during funerals or hospital visits.
8 In France, you *are not* allowed to name a pig 'Napoleon'.

READING

A

Be concise
Give the full story
Be honest
Be accurate
Send a covering letter

B

1 T   2 ?   3 F   4 F   5 F   6 T   7 ?

C

1 boost your chances
2 stand out
3 makes dull reading
4 getting your foot in the door
5 bend the truth

GRAMMAR *Be used to, get used to*

A

1	a	3	b	5 b
2	a	4	a	6 a

B

1	get	3	wearing	5	eating	7	got
2	getting	4	'm	6	used	8	to

DEVELOPING WRITING More formal writing – a covering letter

A

1 *Dear (name)*
2 *Dear Sir or Madam*
3 *Yours sincerely*
4 *Yours faithfully.*

B

1 Refer to a specific job with a job title and /or job reference.
2 Confirm your contact details.
3 Show that you have relevant qualifications.

C

1 *I am writing in response to your job* for a Tourist Information Officer (reference IO1791)
2 *I am available for interview at any time and please do not hesitate to contact me for further information.* I can be contacted on my mobile: 08614 308692, or at home on 01855 593410.
3 *As you can see from my CV,* I have a degree in French and Spanish, and a diploma in Tourism Management. I also have knowledge of several computer programs, and I am currently learning Italian.

D

1 I can be contacted ...
2 I also have knowledge of ...
3 I am available for interview ...
4 I am enclosing my CV for your consideration.
5 I have been in sole charge of ...
6 I am writing in response to ...
7 I look forward to hearing from you.

E

Student's own answers.

VOCABULARY BUILDER QUIZ 5

A

1	finances	3	delivery	5 accounts
2	bonus	4	deadline	6 training

B

1	research	3	blackmail	5 risk
2	support	4	dust	6 demand

C

1	swearing	3	accounts	5 responsible
2	bonuses	4	order	6 contracted

D

1 put in charge of
2 deadline
3 with more variety
4 handed in my notice
5 put up with
6 handle
7 do any lifting

UNIT 6

VOCABULARY Describing souvenirs and presents

A

1	leather	3	silver	5 silk
2	wooden	4	clay	6 plastic

B

1 A: lovely, hand-printed
  B: nice, little
2 A: traditional, hand-made
  B: horrible, machine-woven
3 A: gorgeous, hand-painted
  B: tacky, little
4 B: cute, hand-woven

DEVELOPING CONVERSATIONS Avoiding repetition

1 Can I have a look at those gloves? The red leather *ones* next to the black bag.
2 This belt is made of leather whereas that *one* is made of plastic.
3 I'll take the large bottle of water unless you have any smaller *ones*.
4 Don't you have any paper bags? I hate using plastic *ones*.
5 These machine-woven rugs are in the sale whereas those hand-woven *ones* aren't
6 I'm not sure which ring to choose. I like the gold *one* but it's much more expensive than the silver *one*.

LISTENING

A

silk scarf
silk shirt
laptop
iPod
Chinese herbs, spices & sauces
chopsticks
two kites

B

silk scarf Emma
silk shirt Jodie
laptop Nick
iPod Nick
Chinese herbs, spices & sauces Eddie & Emma
chopsticks Eddie
two kites Emma's children

PRONUNCIATION Intonation on question tags

A

1	weren't you	3	don't they	5 don't you
2	have you	4	did he	6 aren't they

C

1 weren't you ... falling
2 have you ... rising
3 don't they ... falling
4 did he ... rising
5 don't you ... rising
6 aren't they ... falling

DEVELOPING WRITING Using the right tone – complaining

A

1 is for other shoppers
2 is for an Internet company to read

B

1 placed	5 quality	9 regular
2 charge	6 helpdesk	10 unacceptable
3 delay	7 resolve	11 grateful
4 warehouse	8 make	12 courier

C

Student's own answer.

VOCABULARY Clothes and accessories

A

1 scarf, thick jumper, leggings, boots, gloves, woolly jumper, jacket
2 tracksuit, trainers, leggings
3 watch, belt, chain, ring
4 skirt, dress, high heels
5 sandals, trainers, boots, high heels
6 ring, necklace, bracelet, chain, earrings

B

1 bright	5 trendy	9 fit
2 colourful	6 cool	10 tight
3 smart	7 suits	11 go
4 nice	8 match	

READING

A

b How supermarkets get you to spend

B

ice cream: in the middle
potatoes: near the entrance
chewing gum: at the checkout
milk: around the walls and outer part of the store
roses: near the entrance
trolleys and baskets: at the doors
bread: at the back
strawberries: near the entrance
a tin of tomatoes: towards the middle
a magazine: at the checkout

C

1 T	2 T	3 T	4 T	5 T	7 T

D

1 free samples	5 picked up
2 special offers	6 queue up
3 trolley	7 checkout
4 aisles	

GRAMMAR *Must*

A

1 must be going
2 must be freezing
3 must be stuck
4 must have a sale
5 must love shopping
6 must train for hours
7 must be fed up
8 must take her ages

B

1 You really must check out the new shopping mall.
2 You simply must go to the market for your souvenirs.
3 You must try the local wine when you're in Valencia.
  When you're in Valencia, you must try the local wine.
4 You must visit the old town while you're on holiday here.
5 You really must go to the fish restaurant for dinner.

C

1 mustn't	5 had to
2 had to	6 will have to
3 will have to	7 must
4 mustn't	8 will have to

D

At work

1 a	2 a	3 b

At home

4 a	5 b	6 b

DEVELOPING CONVERSATIONS Responding to recommendations

A

Conversation 1

A: I'm thinking of buying some souvenirs before we head home.
B: Well, you could try the old town. There are lots of gift shops there.
C: No, you don't want to go there. It's a rip-off. You'd be better going the market. They have lots of nice handmade stuff there.

Conversation 2

A: I'd like to get some tickets for the new James Bond film next week.
B: Well, go early to queue and get tickets. Lots of people want to see it.
C: No, he doesn't want to do that. You can pre-book at the cinema now. I'd go online and check out their website.

VOCABULARY BUILDER QUIZ 6

A

1 Here's the €20 I *owe* you.
2 I don't often wear bright colours. Most of my clothes are pretty *plain*.
3 Which *brand* of coffee do you usually buy?
4 We bought a beautiful *carved* wooden box in Bali.
5 Have you been to the new shopping *mall* yet?
6 She got married in a lovely *silk* dress.
7 Apparently, there are a lot of *fake* £20 notes going around.
8 It's boiling. Why are you wearing such a *thick* jumper?

B

1 e	2 a	3 b	4 d	5 f	6 c

C

1 out of the game
2 out of date / out of fashion
3 out of danger
4 out of date
5 out of the class
6 out of hospital

D

1 fit	3 queue	5 mass
2 match	4 label	

UNIT 7

VOCABULARY Describing courses

A

1 b   2 c   3 e   4 d   5 a   6 f

B

1 modules   4 tutor   7 essay
2 deadline   5 exams   8 workload
3 lecture   6 seminar

C

1 modules   3 deadline   5 lecture
2 tutor/s   4 seminar   6 essay

DEVELOPING CONVERSATIONS *How's the course going?*

1 hard struggling   4 had term
2 well making   5 final revision
3 Really it   6 hand miss

GRAMMAR *After, once and when*

A

1 correct
2 What are you planning to do after your evening course finishes?
3 Once I meet the other students on the course, I'll feel less nervous.
4 I hope to extend the essay deadline once I *speak* to my tutor.
5 correct
6 When the tutor *arrives*, we'll start the seminar.
7 We're going to have a huge party when the final exams *are* over.
8 After I *leave* college, I'll get a part-time job.

B

1 'll be, it's finished
2 'll let, receive
3 'll come, 've done
4 'll feel, 've got
5 hand, 'll catch
6 'll apologise, see

VOCABULARY Forming words

A

a social
b management
c knowledge
d cooking
e appearance
f ability
g communication
h understanding
i relationships

B

Student's own answers.

C

1 education   6 treatment
2 information   7 elections
3 failure   8 technical
4 practical   9 ability
5 calculations   10 arguments

LISTENING

A

home education   4
'whole child' education   6
the role of teachers   2
the role of parents   5
discipline   3
boarding school   1

B

Opinions 1, 2, 3, 5, and 8

PRONUNCIATION Word stress

A

1 inspiration encourage
2 education
3 educate
4 encouragement inspire co-operate
5 co-operation

READING

A

b

B

1 T   2 F   3 T   4 F   5 T   6 F   7 F

C

1 on   2 in   3 for   4 for   5 in, at   6 in

VOCABULARY Schools, teachers and students

A

1 hardly any facilities
2 had a good reputation
3 Discipline wasn't very good
4 a very good head teacher
5 a bright girl and she's very studious
6 skipping classes

B

A: What's your new French teacher like?
B: Much better than our old teacher. She was quite traditio*nal*. I really enjoy Mr Holland's lessons. He's lively and he *makes* things fun. But he's good at control*ling* the class, too. You know Sharon Dodd, the one who never *pays* attention in class?
A: Oh I know her – she thinks she knows *it all*.
B: Yeah right, well she was messing about and he sent her to the head teacher straightaway.
A: Good for him.
B: So what's your new football coach like?
A: He's good. He really push*es* us in the training sessions and he's very encourag*ing* when we play well. But he's quite patient if we make mistakes.
B: Sounds great.

GRAMMAR Zero conditionals and first conditionals

A

1 f   2 c   3 b   4 e   5 d   6 a

B

1 start, meet
2 might call, have
3 get, won't pass
4 take, get
5 continues, will be suspended

6 might get, download
7 fancy, will be
8 misbehaves, will send

DEVELOPING WRITING A course review – giving feedback

A

A

B

1 thoroughly	6 worksheet
2 experience	7 support
3 standard	8 facilities
4 run	9 achievement
5 rewarding.	10 recommend

C

1 I was hoping for some practical sessions, but the three days consisted of long lectures with no group work.
2 Overall, I thought the training was quite poor.
3 The content of the first day was inappropriate for postgraduate students – it was more undergraduate level.
4 the tutors didn't appear to know how to use the interactive whiteboard, or even the microphone.
5 We were given a very tight deadline for the end-of-course essay and I struggled to get it finished.
6 Perhaps you could review the course content and choice of tutor for future courses.

D

Student's own answers.

VOCABULARY BUILDER QUIZ 7

A

1 assessment	4 achievement
2 dedication	5 observation
3 distractions	6 encouragement

B

convenient
experienced
sensitive
complete
accurate
decisive

C

1 hand in my assignment
   extend the deadline
2 do some revision
   go through the notes
3 pay attention
   get a detention

D

1 N 2 N 3 P 4 P 5 P 6 N 7 N

UNIT 8

VOCABULARY Describing food

A

1 steam boil	4 slice marinate
2 deep-fry stir-fry	5 roast grill
3 mash grate	

B

1 cake	3 bread	5 trifle	7 salad	9 rice
2 sauce	4 soup	6 eggs	8 oysters	10 fruit

C

1 fattening	3 tasty	5 bland
2 spicy	4 greasy	6 filling

D

1 limes	3 trifle	5 blue cheese
2 tripe	4 peanuts	

DEVELOPING CONVERSATIONS Describing dishes

1 It's a kind of fruit. It's a bit like a lemon but it's
2 It's a kind of spice but it's not as strong
3 It's a kind of, it's made from mashed
4 It's a bit like cheese but it's made from mashed soya beans
5 It's a kind of sausage from, It's made from pork

READING

A

b

B

1 B D	3 A	5 C	7 B	9 B
2 A B D	4 B	6 A B C	8 D	10 B D

C

1 bite to eat
2 missed out on
3 from scratch
4 go all day without food
5 proper
6 counts
7 appetite
8 A lack of

GRAMMAR Tend to

A

1 I don't tend to / tend not to have a proper breakfast every morning.
2 We don't tend to split the bill when we eat out.
3 As kids, we didn't tend to / tended not to eat lots of sugary snacks.
4 Since his illness, he hasn't tended to / has tended not to pay attention to his diet.
5 My mum doesn't tend to / tends not to use a recipe book when she cooks.
6 As a student, she didn't tend to / tended not to eat tinned and frozen food.

B

1 tend to
2 didn't tend to
3 tend to
4 tended to
5 would tend to
6 tended to
7 don't tend to/ tend not to
8 doesn't tend to/tends not to

LISTENING

Cheesy pasta with spinach
Serves: 4
Ingredients
 a 200 grams
 b 450 grams
 c butter

d grated
e boiling
f 12
g medium
h spinach
i steam
j olives
k prawns

PRONUNCIATION Long vowel sounds

B

1 /uː/   2 /iː/   3 /ɔː/   4 /ɜː/   5 /ɑː/

C

1 foreign   2 marinate   3 rich   4 décor   5 tough

DEVELOPING WRITING An encyclopedia entry – describing food culture

A

You can buy sushi all over the world now but it won't be as good as in Japan.
I'm really worried that our traditional cuisine may be changing because of imported food.
It's a silly mistake that foreigners make.

B

1 Pasta is a *staple* of the Italian diet.
2 The Polish eat a large *variety* of pork dishes.
3 Fish and seafood *feature* strongly in the coastal areas of Spain.
4 The best-*known* dishes in Argentina are *asado*s.
5 The food in Hong Kong consists *of* a huge range of ingredients.
6 Duck is popular in Singapore served with a range of side *dishes*.
7 Lunch is the *main* meal of the day in Brazil.
8 It's bad *manners* to start eating before the other people at the table.

C

Student's own answers.

VOCABULARY Restaurants

A

1 At St Germain *all the food is very rich.*
2 The Gallery looks out over some beautiful gardens.
3 Casa Paco is always packed.
4 The Olive Tree has got fashionable décor.
5 Sea and Surf only does seafood.

B

1 home-style   5 limited
2 huge   6 organic
3 greasy   7 inviting
4 tough

VOCABULARY *over-*

1 did   5 estimated
2 slept   6 heated
3 cooked   7 reacted
4 charged   8 ate

GRAMMAR Second conditionals

A

1 b   2 a   3 d   4 e   5 f   6 c

B

1

1 would
2 invited
3 might
4 was
5 wouldn't

2

6 was running
7 I'd
8 was
9 I'd expect

3

10 wouldn't
11 were
12 wasn't driving
13 I could

VOCABULARY BUILDER QUIZ 8

A

inviting
filling
raw
tender
mouldy
tough

B

1 juicy   2 crunchy   3 spicy   4 chewy   5 crunchy

C

1 appetite   2 transfer   3 overpower   4 go for   5 sugary

D

1 stock   2 banned   3 bland   4 side   5 packed   6 bare

E

1 goods   2 dish   3 round

UNIT 9

VOCABULARY Describing where you live

A

1 garage
2 back garden
3 swimming pool
4 roof terrace
5 gas central heating
6 basement

B

1 tiled   3 loft   5 patio
2 fire   4 balcony   6 courtyard

C

1 a shared flat, affordable
2 conveniently located, bright
3 run-down, spacious
4 newly built, compact
5 central, cramped

DEVELOPING CONVERSATIONS Making comparisons

1 tiny half size
2 as one wider
3 cramped maybe little

4 about twice mine
5 huge three yours
6 spacious similar bigger

READING

A

1 two women in Vancouver
2 a young guy
3 the development officer
4 Kyle
5 Kyle and his girlfriend
6 Corbin Bernson
7 500 people from Kipling
8 Kyle
9 Corbin Bernsen

B

search
Keep
vacant
face to face
attract
warm welcome

VOCABULARY Describing changes

A

1 c   2 f   3 e   4 d   5 a   6 b

B

1 Unemployment has gone up a lot.
2 Our profits have risen by about 20 per cent.
3 mortgage payments have increased dramatically
4 food prices have gone up a bit
5 property prices have fallen dramatically
6 the cost of energy has dropped steadily

C

1 rates   5 dramatic
2 take   6 protect
3 in   7 gets
4 investments   8 tackling

LISTENING

A

1 29   3 affordable   5 doesn't tell
2 ten   4 Lylle

B

The flat was:
too expensive 6
tiny 1
very cold 2
in bad condition 4
quite a long way from the underground 3
not very clean 5

PRONUNCIATION Correcting information

A

1 You couldn't call it <u>compact</u>; it was just <u>cramped</u>.
2 It's wasn't <u>chilly</u>; it was <u>freezing</u>.
3 The agent said it was <u>ten</u> minutes from the tube, but it was more like <u>20</u>.
4 It was supposed to be <u>affordable</u> but that's just <u>overpriced</u>.

C

1 d   2 e   3 a   4 b   5 c

VOCABULARY Describing areas

1 lively, noisy, dead
2 rough, dirty, residential, posh
3 green, isolated, convenient

GRAMMAR Comparing the past with now

A

1 rougher   3 more   5 as
2 than   4 nowhere   6 noisy

B

1 Life is more complicated than it used to be
2 The air in the town is much less polluted
3 House prices are not as high as they were
4 There is much more traffic than there used to be
5 There are far fewer businesses in the city centre
6 There is less tourism than before

C

1 more   4 was   7 more   10 fewer
2 than   5 much   8 much   11 nowhere
3 be   6 longer 9 before   12 are

DEVELOPING CONVERSATIONS Polite requests

1 Is as
2 mind Not at all
3 Can not
4 Would within
5 Would depends
6 have Obviously

DEVELOPING WRITING A room advert – checking accuracy

A

4 a   5 b   1 c   3 d   2 e   6 f

B

quiet
located
consists of
bright
central
looking for
noisy

C

Student's own answers.

VOCABULARY BUILDER QUIZ 9

A

1 posh   2 green   3 separate   4 compact

B

The roof is leaking.
There's a shortage of affordable housing.
There were hardly any volunteers for the clean-up campaign.
The building project has gone over budget.
The central heating needs fixing.
The graffiti in the area put off potential buyers.

C

1 b   2 d   3 a   4 f   5 e   6 c

D

1 rent   2 aim   3 rise   4 profit

E

1 elections
2 improvements
3 innovative
4 connected
5 investment

UNIT 10

VOCABULARY Films, exhibitions and plays

A

Aspects of a film
  soundtrack
  special effects
  plot
Types of painting
  still life
  portrait
  landscape
Exhibitions
  photography
  installation
  sculpture
  video artist
Types of play
  drama
  comedy
  tragedy
  historical play

B

1 gig lighting audience
2 director acting costumes scenery
3 trailer horror films romantic comedy thriller
4 painting painter abstract

C

1 What's on?
2 What kind of exhibition is it? / What is it a collection of?
3 What's the play about?
4 Where's the exhibition on?
5 When's it on?
6 Who's in it?

DEVELOPING CONVERSATIONS Explaining where things are

1 off
2 coming
3 halfway
4 back
5 right
6 in front
7 at
8 next
9 out
10 towards
11 facing

LISTENING

A

1 c   2 b   3 a   4 a   5 b   6 c

PRONUNCIATION Same sound or different?

1 D   2 S   3 D   4 D   5 D   6 D

VOCABULARY Describing what's on

A

1 amazing
2 trendy
3 spectacular
4 touristy
5 incredible
6 marvellous

B

6 a play
5 an exhibition
1 a film
4 a dance show
3 a rugby match
2 a restaurant

C

1 dull
2 terrible
3 dreadful
4 brilliant
5 weird
6 terrific

D

1 e   2 c   3 f   4 d   5 b   6 a

DEVELOPING CONVERSATIONS Why you do not want to do things

A

1 of   2 right   3 is   4 any   5 to   6 self

B

1 I don't really feel like it.
2 it's not really my kind of thing.
3 it sounds a bit too trendy for me.
4 it sounds a bit too weird for me.
5 it looks a bit too touristy for me.
6 I'm not really in the mood for that kind of thing.

READING

A

a

B

1 T   2 T   3 DS   4 F   5 T   6 F   7 F

C

1 g   3 h   5 d   7 e
2 a   4 c   6 f   8 b

VOCABULARY Describing an event

1 overrated, saying, moving, tears, out.
2 through, rubbish, atmosphere, everything.
3 trendy, place, packed, hot, crazy
4 weird, why

GRAMMAR The future in the past

A

1 She said she was going to meet some friends at the cinema.
2 He promised he'd get the theatre tickets online.
3 She didn't think the gig would be very good.
4 He promised he wouldn't be late for the party.
5 The manager said the gig would probably finish at about 11.30.
6 She thought that all the clubs were going to be packed.

B

wouldn't / spend
might / come supposed / arrive
1 was going to ring
2 might come
3 were supposed to arrive
4 wouldn't spend

WRITING Emails – arranging to go out

A

A 1 know   2 coming   3 get
B 1 dull   2 reviews   3 excuses   4 tickets
C 1 come   2 make   3 way
D 1 nice   2 kind   3 ever
E 1 supposed   2 fancy   3 on   4 out

B

A 5   B 3   C 4   D 2   E 1

Vocabulary Builder Quiz 10

A

1 cast
2 audience
3 portrait / landscape / still life
4 sculpture
5 trailer
6 plot

B

1 congratulations
2 decorations
3 demonstration
4 possessions
5 suggestion
6 option

C

1 I'm not very *keen* on modern art.
2 I'll give you a *lift* to the station if you like.
3 It was awful. She burst into *tears* when she heard the news.
4 The late *showing* of the film doesn't finish until after midnight.
5 Take the next *turning* on the left.
6 He always *fails* to understand what I'm trying to say.

D

Possible answers:

1 weird
2 terrible / dreadful
3 brilliant / terrific / amazing / fantastic
4 terrific / amazing / trendy / spectacular / exclusive
5 spectacular / incredible
6 dreadful
7 authentic

UNIT 11

Vocabulary Animals

A

1 bear   3 dolphin   5 crow
2 parrot   4 wolf   6 whale

B

1 squirrels   3 cockroaches   5 crocodiles
2 lizards   4 eagles   6 deer

Developing conversations Helping to tell stories

1
2 Well it was rush hour and I was driving home from the office when I suddenly saw a deer in the road.
3 I guess it had come out of the forest that stretches along the side of the road. The poor animal looked really scared and confused.
4 So what happened in the end?
1 You'll never guess what happened last night.
5 Well, the police and wildlife officers were going to tranquilise it, but they couldn't shoot at it because there was still a lot of traffic around.

2
5 Nobody knows. But it had hidden so deeply inside the engine that they had to take it apart to get the cat out. It had been there for a week without food or water and the guy had driven 300 miles!
1 Did you hear about that cat that spent a week stuck in a car engine?
7 No, it was amazing. It just had a few minor burns on its fur.
8 So what happened in the end?
2 No, where was that?

9 The guy gave the cat back to his neighbour. Apparently, it was fine, despite what had happened.
3 I think it was in Austria. This guy heard a sound coming from his Mercedes so he looked under the bonnet and found his neighbour's cat.
4 But what was it doing there?
6 Seriously? Not hurt or anything?

Grammar *-ing* clauses

A

1 circling   diving
2 crawling   biting
3 barking   singing
4 lying   sitting
5 living   running
6 learning   catching

Listening

c, f, b, d, a, e

Pronunciation Same pronunciation, different spelling

1 son   sun
2 weather   whether
3 break   brake
4 red   read
5 write   right
6 wait   weight

Grammar Passives

A

1 is covered   B
2 is known   A
3 are known   C
4 are used   C
5 have been developed   A
6 were bred   A
7 was adopted   A
8 are threatened   B

B

1 A new shopping centre is being built in the centre of town.
2 The diamonds were smuggled out of the country in bags of sugar.
3 The photocopier was being repaired all yesterday morning.
4 Students are graded according to their age and ability.
5 All civil servants have been given a pay rise.
6 The new president will be interviewed on live TV.

Reading

A

wheat   cotton   papyrus   foxglove

B

Which plant
1 D
2 A   B
3 B
4 C
5 A
6 D
7 A   B   C
8 C

C

1 vital	3 originated	5 crops
2 made	4 portable	6 had

VOCABULARY Keeping pets

A

1
1 looking after
2 puppies
3 to an enormous size
4 exercise
5 leftovers
6 dry food
7 mess
8 scratch
9 jump
10 lick

2

1	big	7	play
2	kittens	8	noise
3	outside	9	food
4	attention	10	smelly
5	aggressive	11	litter tray
6	hold	12	playful

B

1 poisonous	5 tank
2 demanding	6 regularly
3 babies	7 mice
4 to	

VOCABULARY Forming words

A

1 investigations	5 freedom
2 threatened	6 warnings
3 extinction	7 independence
4 destruction	

B

e + -ation
combination
imagination

+ -dom
boredom
kingdom

+ -en
lengthen
frighten

+ -ing
spelling
meeting

+ -ion
direction
correction

t+ -ce
convenience
relevance

DEVELOPING WRITING A blog – giving an opinion

A

1 against	5 treat	9 get	13 like
2 point	6 What	10 mean	14 I take
3 me	7 see	11 fact	
4 make	8 couldn't	12 forget	

VOCABULARY BUILDER QUIZ 11

A

1 c   2 e   3 d   4 a   5 b

B

1 point   2 under   3 free   4 role

C

1 scratch	2 tank	3 grass
4 habitat	5 breeds	6 destruction

D

1 will be released	4 was banned
2 were arrested	5 was moved
3 are threatened	6 will be suspended

E

1 crawl   2 trek   3 search   4 hunt

UNIT 12

VOCABULARY Describing character

A

1 stubborn	2 generous
3 chatty	4 bright
5 spoilt	6 easy-going
7 intense	8 naughty

Hidden word: outgoing

B

1 sweet	2 shy
3 affectionate	4 indulgent
5 competitive	6 determined
7 lazy	

C

Student's own answers

DEVELOPING CONVERSATIONS That's like …

1 B   2 E   3 C   4 D   5 A

READING

A

1 d   2 f   3 b   4 e   5 a   6 c

B

1 F   2 T   3 T   4 T   5 T   6 F

C

1 f   2 d   3 b   4 e   5 a   6 c

GRAMMAR Used to and would

A

1 was	3 would	5 didn't	7 would
2 used to	4 played	6 was	8 wasn't

B

1 Amy used to be very competitive. She would spend / spent hours preparing for tests

2 My dad used to work shifts. He would leave / left the house while we were all asleep.

3 Elisa used to collect coins. She had about 500 from different countries

4 I used to be very close to my granddad. We would spend / spent hours together working in his garden.

5 Adam used to be quite spoilt. He would get / got anything he asked for.

6 This area used to be quite rough. People would throw/ threw their litter all over the place.

VOCABULARY Synonyms

A

stay + example: *together*
in bed all day
in touch

remain + example: *in power*
a big challenge
a serious problem

maintain
a conversation
a friendship
a long-distance relationship

keep
in touch
something warm
forgetting

B

1 keep stay   remain
2 stayed   remained
3 keeps
4 keep   stay
5 keep   stay
6 keep
7 stay   keep

C

1	remained	Students own answer
2	keep	Students own answer
3	maintained	Students own answer
4	remains	Students own answer
5	stay	Students own answer
6	maintains	Students own answer
7	remain	Students own answer

GRAMMAR Expressing regrets (*wish*)

A

1 I got stuck in a traffic jam for hours. I wish I'd gone by train.

2 My first boyfriend was really selfish and big-headed. I wish I'd never met him.

3 These shoes fell apart after two weeks. I wish I'd never bought them.

4 The meal was tasty but a bit greasy. I wish I hadn't fried the chicken.

5 I slipped and broke my leg on the first day. I wish I'd never tried skiing.

6 I like my open fire but it takes ages to warm up the room. I wish we had put in central heating.

7 I have an enormous workload and tight deadlines. I wish I wish I had chosen a different course.

8 We left the film halfway through because my son was scared. I wish they had warned me about the special effects.

B

1 I wish I hadn't fallen out with my dad.
2 I wish I had visited Brazil.
3 I wish I'd married the love of my life.
4 I wish I hadn't been late for my son's graduation.
5 I wish I hadn't left my degree course.
6 I wish I had spent time with my kids.

1 f Not resolving arguments
2 d Not seeing important places
3 e Not choosing the right partner
4 b Missing experiences
5 a Not achieving potential
6 c Missing family growing up

DEVELOPING WRITING A profile – describing a person

A

1	Although	2	when
3	as	4	Because of
5	While	6	so that
7	despite		

B

1 Although I was quite naughty at school, my parents still believed in me.

2 My coach made me a determined person so that I became a professional footballer.

3 Despite having a lot of problems, my friends always supported me.

4 While I was missing my parents, my sister was always there for me.

5 I never lost hope because my dad had been such a good role model.

6 When I was feeling down, she would always cheer me up.

C

Students own answer.

LISTENING

A

1990s
150
five
Internet
thousands
famous
five
friendships

B

1 T	2 F	3 T	4 T
5 F	6 T	7 F	8 F

PRONUNCIATION Connected speech

A

1 I have hundreds of friends all over the world.
2 I have friends at college that I meet up with every day.
3 I have a lot of colleagues and a big circle of acquaintances.
4 We keep in touch as much as possible.
5 Well, I'm a bit of a loner.
6 My circle of friends is quite small.
7 I'm quite outgoing and chatty.
8 I've also made a lot of new friends on my course.

Vocabulary Builder Quiz 12

A

1 out   2 great   3 check   4 off   5 step   6 easy

B

1 c   2 f   3 d   4 a   5 b   6 e

C

1 down   2 out   3 in

D

1 confident   4 intense / stressed
2 affectionate   5 generous
3 kind / thoughtful

E

1 idiotic   4 powerful
2 determined   5 egoistic
3 demonstration

UNIT 13

Vocabulary Ways of travelling and travel problems

A

1 day   4 school
2 light   5 travelling
3 journey   6 shopping

B

1 platform   line   carriage
2 crossing   deck   harbour
3 traffic lights bend   tyre
4 take-off   check-in desk security

C

1 stupid   4 slippery
2 bumpy   5 wrong
3 huge   6 terrifying

Listening

A

b

B

1 c   2 a   3 b   4 a   5 c   6 b

Pronunciation

A

1 ev**e**ryday
2 profess**i**onal bus**i**ness
3 av**e**rage trav**e**lling
4 diff**e**rent
5 trav**e**llers

B

1 carr**i**age
2 pref**e**rably
3 sev**e**ral
4 uncomf**or**table
5 int**e**resting

Vocabulary Phrasal verbs

1 hanging around   5 pour down
2 check in   6 calm down
3 worked out   7 got back
4 set off   8 go through

Grammar Third conditionals

A

1 'd   3 could   5 wouldn't
2 hadn't   4 hadn't   6 have

B

1 B: If he'd checked the details before, he would *have* caught his plane.
2 B: If she hadn't emigrated to Canada, we might have *kept* in touch.
3 B: If I *had* been able to get a signal on my mobile, I would have let you know.
4 B: We could have caught the bus to the hotel if you *hadn't* hung around for so long.
5 B: To be honest, we'd have stayed in the UK if there hadn't *been* so much unemployment.
6 B: If I hadn't agreed, they wouldn't *have* allowed me on the plane.

Reading

A

1 c   2 a   3 d   4 b

C

1 Gorongosa National Park, Mozambique
2 Mount Elgon, Kenya
3 Bikini Atoll, an island in the Pacific Ocean
4 The Panama Railway
5 Bikini Atoll, an island in the Pacific Ocean
6 Mount Elgon, Kenya
7 The Panama Railway
8 Gorongosa National Park, Mozambique

D

The year the nuclear tests ended
Length of the train ride on the Panama Railway
The drive from Nairobi to Mount Elgon National Park
Depth of the caves in the mountain in Mount Elgon, Kenya
Visitors to Gorongosa National Park, Mozambique in 1971
Height of Mount Gorongosa, Mozambique

E

1 trek   4 hikers
2 turned   5 feature
3 tensions, eased   6 unspoilt

Vocabulary Strong adjectives

A

1 delicious   4 furious
2 boiling   5 huge
3 fascinating   6 starving

B

1 really fantastic
2 completely soaked
3 absolutely exhausting
4 really filthy
5 absolutely packed
6 absolutely freezing

Grammar Should have

1 We should've set off earlier.
2 You shouldn't have worn high-heels.
3 He should have applied for it earlier.
4 I shouldn't have packed so much stuff.
5 You shouldn't have stayed up so late.
6 She should've asked for an extension.

7 You should've asked someone for directions.
8 We shouldn't have made so much noise.

DEVELOPING CONVERSATIONS Blaming people

1 me   5 blame   9 fault
2 fault   6 should've   10 should've
3 kids   7 hers   11 nobody's
4 told   8 she'd   12 happened

DEVELOPING WRITING A description – using interesting language

A

see (underlined)
hear (bold)
smell (italics)

Our journey started on [1] an empty railway platform. The temperature had dropped to minus 3° the night before and it was still [2] very cold. I was [3] very tired after a [4] bad night's sleep and I wasn't looking forward to the trip. **The station was [5] very quiet until the train arrived a few minutes later.** The sun started to rise as we set off and I could see [6] nice stripes of red and orange across the sky. *Suddenly, I could smell hot coffee.* We had skipped breakfast and I realised I was [7] very hungry. At that moment a man appeared selling coffee and [8] big pieces of sweet bread – it was [9] very nice. After a few stops along the line, **we could hear people talking** and laughing. Moments later, our carriage was [10] full of local people going to market. They wore traditional clothes in [11] nice colours and they were very friendly. **They told us [12] interesting stories and gave us advice about the next part of our trip.** By the time we reached our stop, we had made lots of [13] nice new friends.

B

1 a deserted   7 absolutely starving   13 fantastic
2 absolutely freezing   8 huge
3 absolutely exhausted   9 really tasty
4 terrible   10 packed with
5 absolutely silent   11 wonderful
6 beautiful   12 fascinating

C

Students' own answer

VOCABULARY BUILDER QUIZ 13

A

1 line   2 fence   3 traffic lights   4 bump

B

1 useless   3 careless   5 sleepless
2 worthless   4 painless   6 speechless

C

1 up   3 out   5 down
2 up   4 for   6 through

D

1 recharge   3 restrictions   5 reduce
2 reserved   4 reservation   6 reserve

E

1 desk   2 travel   3 security

UNIT 14

VOCABULARY Computers

A

1 scanner   3 hard drive   5 file
2 socket   4 screen   6 cable

B

1 menu   3 printer   5 plug
2 cursor   4 mouse   6 keyboard

C

1 i   3 e   5 c   7 b   9 f
2 h   4 d   6 g   8 a

DEVELOPING CONVERSATIONS Responding to advice

1 work   connection   In that case
2 file   done   work
3 crashed   rebooting   yet   else
4 stop   difference   best

DEVELOPING WRITING An essay – discussing pros and cons

A

b

B

Para 1
The use of computers in education has increased enormously over the last decade.

Para 2
So what are the pros and cons of this revolution in education?

Para 3
On the other hand, there are also problems with computers.

Para 4
In conclusion, I think there is an important role for computers in education, but students also need other learning opportunities.

C

The use of computers in education has increased enormously over the last decade.

There are obviously several benefits to using computers.

On the other hand, there are also problems with computers.

In conclusion, I think there is an important role for computers in education, but students also need other learning opportunities.

D

1 a   2 b   3 a   4 a

E

Student's own answers

VOCABULARY Talking about markets

A

1 g   2 a   3 b   4 c   5 d   6 f   7 e

B

1 is bigger than it was 20 years ago
2 is smaller than it used to be
3 almost saturated

4 tiny
5 growing steadily
6 is smaller than it was 20 years ago

Reading

A
b

B
1 c   2 b   3 c   4 a   5 c   6 b

C
1 moved   3 virtual   5 naked
2 access to   4 digitally   6 armchair

Vocabulary Technology, programs and gadgets

A
1 upgrade powerful design cool lighter carry
2 100GB store allows formats warns a dangerous

B
screen picture
set switch
save automatically
run greener
save efficient
use straightforward

Grammar -ing forms and to-infinitives

1 trying
2 to get
3 to sort out
4 buying
5 using driving
6 having
7 using
8 to accept
9 to send
10 throw away to work

Listening

A
a 5   b 2   c 4   d 6   e 3   f 1

B
1 F   3 F   5 T   7 F   9 F
2 T   4 T   6 F   8 T

Pronunciation

A
1 D   2 S   3 S   4 S   5 D   6 S

Vocabulary Builder Quiz 14

A
1 a cable   3 a key   5 a plug
2 a switch   4 a bulb

B
1 technology   3 back   5 leave
2 make   4 socket   6 run

C
1 We would like to install SOLAR panels in our new house.
2 He SPILLED coffee all over my desk and didn't even clear it up.

3 Can you turn the FAN on – it's boiling in here.
4 Be careful you don't TRIP on the edge of the carpet.
5 Remember to LOG off when you have finished using my computer.
6 How long would it take to SCAN these colour photos?
7 I love my new laptop. It's got some really COOL programs.
8 There was a BITTER dispute between the two families that lasted years.

D
1 computer   3 program   5 skills
2 epidemic   4 scanner   6 post

UNIT 15

Vocabulary Injuries and illness

A
1 a nasty cold sneezing thermometer painkillers
2 coughing flu allergy medicine
3 dizzy sprained support stitches

B
1 rash
2 X-rayed
3 some cream
4 upset stomach
5 high blood pressure
6 cut
7 swollen
8 arthritis
9 antibiotics

Developing conversations Short questions with any

1 Any dizziness?   Any pain?
  Any stiffness?   Any questions?
2 Any vomiting?   Any itchiness?
  Any other symptoms? Any medication?

Listening

1 c   2 a   3 a   4 b

Pronunciation

A
1 /ɒ/ 2 /ʊ/ 3 /ɜ/ 4 /ɪ/ 5 /e/ 6 /ə/ 7 /æ/

B
1 antib**io**tics   5 **fee**l
2 press**ure**   6 **ar**thritis
3 stom**a**ch   7 sh**ou**lder
4 sw**o**llen

Vocabulary Word formation

1 medical   5 addicted
2 viral   6 incurable
3 naturally   7 irritability
4 fatty   8 infectious

Vocabulary Explaining causes and results

A
1 to T
2 linked T
3 get T
4 mean T
5 causes T
6 you go T

7 make   T
8 by   F

READING

A

1 D   2 A   3 E   4 B   5 C

B

1 F   3 DS   5 DS   7 DS   9 DS
2 F   4 T   6 T   8 T

C

1 of   2 of   3 with   4 of   5 in   6 between

VOCABULARY Accidents and problems

1 fell down   ended up with sunburn   bit   crashed into
2 stung   got food poisoning   slipped on   had fainted
3 burnt   fell off   tripped over   bruised

GRAMMAR Reported speech

1 The woman said she wasn't allergic to antibiotics.
2 The surgeon said the operation would last about an hour.
3 The man said he usually took the medicine at night.
4 The parents said they were waiting for their son's test results.
5 The boy said he had broken his leg in a skiing accident.
6 The nurses said they were going to X-ray his ankle as soon as possible.
7 The girl said the dog bit her on the arm.
8 The doctor said I could visit Melanie whenever I liked.
9 The doctor said I had to make an appointment for tests at the hospital.

GRAMMAR Reporting verbs

1 He apologised for not visiting me in hospital.
2 The doctor insisted on checking my blood pressure.
3 The nurse denied that she had given the patient the wrong medication.
4 My neighbour promised to look after everything while I was in hospital.
5 She offered to get my tablets for me.
6 Mum told Ruth not to sunbathe for more than half an hour.
7 My friend suggested I tried yoga to help with stress.
8 The surgeon warned me not to eat or drink anything before my operation.

DEVELOPING WRITING An email – describing an accident / problem

A

the situation before the problem happened   2
the doctor's diagnosis   5
how she feels now   6
how she got to hospital   1
the people who helped her   4
what she was doing when the problem happened   3

B

1 ended up   2 set off
3 'd left   4 would need
5 were eating   6 stood up
7 offered   8 insisted
9 persuaded   10 'll be going

C
Student's own answer

VOCABULARY BUILDER QUIZ 15

A

1 infection   2 stimulant
3 sneeze   4 joints

B

1 to   2 down   3 up   4 off   5 over

C

1 cough   2 attack   3 cure   4 bite   5 sting

D

1 bug   2 disease   3 symptons   4 nasty

E

1 d   2 g   3 a   4 f   5 c   6 b   7 e

UNIT 16

VOCABULARY Newspapers

A

1 h   2 c   3 d   4 f
5 g   6 e   7 a   8 b

B

1 exchange rate
2 premiere
3 ceasefire
4 marks out of ten
5 the score
6 star sign

DEVELOPING CONVERSATIONS *Apparently*

1 Apparently, it sold out in less than five minutes.
2 Apparently, it doesn't use electricity or gas for heating or for any of the equipment.
3 Apparently, in patient tests it was 90 per cent successful.
4 Apparently, she'd never been abroad before.
5 Apparently, the Arctic ice is disappearing more quickly than ever before.

LISTENING

A

Hudson River in New York

B

1 1549
2 15 January 2009
3 155
4 three minutes
5 3 200 feet
6 broken legs
7 US president George Bush
8 day
9 5.5
10 76,000
11 2007
12 219
13 600 million dollars

PRONUNCIATION

A

1 b	3 a	5 a	7 b
2 b	4 b	6 b	8 b

C

1 one / nine
2 one / fifty five
3 three / two
4 nine / seventy five
5 five / five
6 seventy six
7 nineteen
8 six / million

VOCABULARY Explaining who people are

A

1 d   2 e   3 f   4 b   5 c   6 a

B

1 artist   is considered   founder
2 led   founder
3 activist   campaigned   rights
4 doctor   vaccine
5 mathematician   whose
6 athlete   set
7 dictator   responsible
8 studied   discovered

GRAMMAR Defining relative clauses

A

1 c	3 b	5 e	7 g
2 h	4 d	6 f	8 a

B

Christian Dior   2
The Cold War   8
Erasmus   1
Harrods   6
Aretha Franklin   4
The White House   3
Halloween   5
Nasa   7

C

1 who / that
2 which/that
3 where
4 who / that
5 when
6 who / that
7 which / that
8 who / that

D

1
3
6

DEVELOPING WRITING A website entry – an influential person

A

c

B

1 Although   5 not   9 influential
2 for   6 appeal   10 awards

3 who   7 way   11 remains
4 when   8 called   12 that

C

1 led   b
2 revolutionised   h
3 was   d
4 left   g
5 raised   a
6 dedicated   c
7 was   e
8 inspired   f

D

Student's own answer

READING

A

1 d   2 e   3 b   4 a   5 c

B

1 T   5 T   6 T   8 T

C

he = Mr McGowan
his = Mr McGowan's
it = the helicopter
it = the gift (the trip)
this = 'Earth Hour'
then = 2007
the artist = Michael Jackson
one – statue
it = the Pepsi company

D

1 make   5 raise
2 catch   6 imagination
3 media   7 promotional
4 launch   8 promote

VOCABULARY BUILDER QUIZ 16

A

1 c   2 a   3 b   4 d   5 e

B

1 bravery   5 influential
2 dictatorship   6 athletic
3 redundancy   7 unified
4 liberation   8 courageous

C

1 nail   2 glue   3 clip   4 tape

D

1 hit   5 reviews
2 after   6 barrier
3 founded   7 contestant
4 is considered   8 down

CD1		
TRACK	ITEM	
1	titles	
2	1.1	
3	1.2	
4	2.1	Mark
5		Mrs deVere
6		Annie
7	2.2	
8	3.1	Speaker 1
9		Speaker 2
10		Speaker 3
11		Speaker 4
12		Speaker 5
13	3.2	
14	4.1	Part 1
15	4.2	Part 2
16	4.3	
17	5.1	Speaker 1
18		Speaker 2
19		Speaker 3
20		Speaker 4
21		Speaker 5
22	5.2	
23	6.1	
24	6.2	
25	7.1	
26	7.2	
27	8.1	
28	8.2	
29	8.3	
30	9.1	Part 1
31	9.2	Part 2
32	9.3	
33	9.4	
34	10.1	1
35		2
36		3
37		4
38		5
39		6
40	10.2	
41	11.1	
42	11.2	
43	11.3	
44	12.1	Part 1
45	12.2	Part 2
46	12.3	
47	13.1	
48	13.2	
49	13.3	
50	14.1	Part 1
51		Part 2
52		Part 3

CD1		
TRACK	ITEM	
53	14.2	
54	15.1	1
55		2
56		3
57		4
58	15.2	
59	15.3	
60	16.1	
61	16.2	
62	16.3	